Neurofeedback 101

Rewiring the Brain for ADHD,
Anxiety, Depression and Beyond
(without medication)

What Neurofeedback Does
and How it Works

ADHD
Depression
Anxiety
Insomnia
Concussions
PTSD
Autism
Processing
Migraines
Developmental Trauma
...other brain issues

Michael P. Cohen

Our brain's ability to change itself is now unmistakable.

How can anyone turn off years of anxiety,
ADHD or migraines without medication,
just with the help of feedback?

After reading this book, you'll understand
how your brain makes it happen.

DISCLAIMER

Many health care books have disclaimers. So we will, too. The information presented in this book is intended to be a guide to help you. Neither the author nor anyone associated with *Neurofeedback 101*, or the information it contains, claims that it is a substitute for professional medical or mental health care.

Use this book to help you become proactive, ask questions and discuss treatment options with your choice of appropriate professionals. The author, publisher or anyone associated with the *Neurofeedback 101* book, website or any entity under this name is not responsible or liable for any loss or damage allegedly arising from any information or suggestion in the *Neurofeedback 101* book. Our purpose is to educate readers about neurofeedback as a possible treatment or training option for brain-related disorders to enable them to live fuller, happier and healthier lives.

Conditions such as post-traumatic stress disorder (PTSD), trauma, anxiety, migraines, attention deficit/hyperactivity disorder (ADHD), depression, concussions and other brain-based conditions can be serious problems. We recommend you seek qualified professional care for any such conditions.

DEDICATION

This book is dedicated to my wife Carolyn, who has supported me throughout this long and complicated journey, and to all the colleagues who have shared so much in our quest to learn how to help people change their brain and change their life. And thanks to all the clients who sought us out and helped us learn how to help them.

Table of Contents

How (and Why) to Read this Book

There are three main parts of this book. Read in the order that makes sense for you.

Are you most interested in **how** your brain learns from feedback? That's embedded in **Part 1**: **What is neurofeedback and how does it work?**

If you learn best from examples, you might want to start at **Part 2: Discussion of Case Examples**.

If you have lots of questions about neurofeedback, start at **Part 3: Frequently Asked Questions about Neurofeedback**.

Why read this book?

If you're reading this, you're likely either **seeking answers** for significant brain challenges or are **curious** about what neurofeedback is and how it works.

Neurofeedback 101 is meant to be an introduction to neurofeedback for health consumers and health professionals. (It is not meant to teach you how to do neurofeedback.)

Perhaps you read or heard about neurofeedback while searching for alternatives to medications. Maybe you're curious about the brain and a concept known as "neuroplasticity." You might be a health care professional seeking a better understanding of this non-medication option.

If you're like most people investigating neurofeedback, you're wondering:

- Does neurofeedback really work?
- How does neurofeedback work?
- Is neurofeedback a serious alternative to medications?
- How many sessions does it take to achieve results?
- How long do the effects last?
- What issues can neurofeedback help solve?
- Can you do neurofeedback if you're on medication?
- Is there solid research on neurofeedback?
- Is neurofeedback worth my investment of time and money?
- Can neurofeedback harm my brain or make my situation worse?
- If it's so darn good, why isn't everyone using neurofeedback?
- How is neurofeedback different from mindfulness or computer games?
- Is all neurofeedback the same?
- Does neurofeedback ever not work? If so, why does it fail?

I try to answer these and many other questions *as directly and simply as possible* in the pages that follow.

Note: Throughout the book you will see the words "EEG" and "qEEG."

An EEG, or electroencephalogram, is a non-invasive test used to evaluate the electrical activity in the brain.

A qEEG, short for quantitative electroencephalogram, is another term for an EEG-based brain map. It's a digital analysis of the EEG that typically compares an individual's EEG patterns to statistical normative data (how you compare to other people in your age range).

Foreword
by Robert P. "Rusty" Turner, M.D.

Note: Dr. Turner has been a neurologist for 30 years, specializing in epilepsy and neurological disorders in children and adults. He's taught at major medical schools and conferences around the world. He explains his enthusiasm for neurofeedback as a valuable tool and why he feels this book is important.

I've had a lifelong passion for clinical medicine and academic excellence. However, over the years I gradually became disillusioned with the limited toolbox available for treating epilepsy and neurological disorders. These tools are comprised primarily of medications (pharmacotherapy) and, sometimes, surgical interventions. They rarely address the underlying causes of illness. Their effectiveness is often limited for many patients and can create unwanted side effects.

Beginning in 2010 I started extensively researching scientific and evidence-based literature about neurofeedback (EEG biofeedback). Even though it's frequently dismissed by the medical community, the initial evidence compelled me to dig further.

I learned about the early seizure work of UCLA scientist and neurofeedback pioneer M. Barry Sterman Ph.D. His seminal research riveted my attention. His findings showed evidence that neurofeedback could reduce seizures in both animal and human models. I saw claims that neurofeedback could also improve other brain-related symptoms, including headaches/ migraines, anxiety, concussions, depression, ADHD and more.

If it was real, I wanted to investigate it beyond just review- ing the research and literature. I met with clinicians and some of their clients and patients whose lives had been changed by neurofeedback.

I also went to neurofeedback courses and conferences. At one of those conferences, I met Mike Cohen after a presenta- tion he gave. I found him engaging, helpful and, above all, experienced and knowledgeable. We immediately clicked.

As time went on, the more I heard and the more I studied, the more compelling the evidence became.

Eventually I took a leap of faith and pursued a six-month research and training sabbatical from my position at the med- ical center where I'd worked for 17 years. The end result—I left my academic position and opened a neurology practice specializing in neurodiagnostic testing (EEG and quantitative EEG analysis) and neurofeedback.

It was a bold move, because at the time I knew of only three neurologists and one neurosurgeon involved in neurofeed- back. The risk, however, was worth it. Being able to offer neurofeedback, along with some other evidence-based com- plementary and alternative approaches, resulted in the lives of many of my patients being transformed in ways I'd never seen before. For the first time in my medical career I felt like a true health care provider instead of just a disease manager.

I was delighted when Mike asked me to write the foreword to this book. He's respected as a provider and teacher through- out much of the neurofeedback community. It's also a book that is needed.

When I read his manuscript, I remember wishing there'd been a book like *Neurofeedback 101* when I started my research.

It's an excellent overview of how neurofeedback works and its impact. It's an easy read—not too complicated nor oversimplified. I found the FAQ section superb, and the case histories corroborated over and over the experiences I've witnessed with my own patients.

I also thought it was important for readers to know that there _are_ physicians "out there" who are supportive of neurofeedback. We work to harness what's known as neuroplasticity to help our patients. Neuroplasticity is the brain's lifelong ability to grow, change and heal.

Those of us who know what neurofeedback can do want as many people as possible to learn about it. This book is the perfect tool to achieve that end.

I frequently ask myself why, if neurofeedback has been around for decades and has an evidence-based foundation, isn't it more mainstream. Why is it not being offered more broadly around the world? Mike tackles that question, and many more, in the book.

Unfortunately, many health professionals are unfamiliar with it. Some say that it doesn't work, or it's not evidence-based, or it's experimental. Yet I know from years of dedicated study and clinical application that neurofeedback works.

Neurofeedback is an amazing health care intervention, and Mike's book is a valuable overview for anyone who has a personal or professional interest in it.

--Robert P. "Rusty" Turner M.D.,
Founder, Network Neurology and Network Neurology
Health, LLC
M.S.C.R. (Master of Science in Clinical Research)
Charleston, South Carolina

Preface

The challenge of writing about neurofeedback

For much of my career, I searched for a simple explanation for the question: "How does neurofeedback REALLY work?"

Some years ago, I created a popular four-minute YouTube video called "What Is Neurofeedback?[1]" Many clinicians still use that as a simple introduction to this technology.

It's a start. But it isn't nearly enough to tell the whole story.

By giving instant feedback about your brain activity while you train, neurofeedback provides information that your brain learns from. That's the technology, very simplified.

But how can your brain change or learn from that feedback? That's the interesting and exciting part. It's also the hardest concept for people to understand. It can be counterintuitive.

How I Decided to Go into the Neurofeedback Field

It began with a family crisis.

In 1995, I was enjoying a successful career in the high-tech industry in Atlanta where I worked as a software consultant for very complex systems. Although I was doing well, my father was not.

---

[1] https://youtu.be/HxHR7InSQ1c

Untreatable depression

Suffering from a severe type of depression, he had been treated for years with medication, psychotherapy and dietary changes. He had even undergone shock treatments. Nothing we tried helped. He had constant, severe, unrelenting agitation, with virtually zero quality of life. He couldn't hold a conversation, read a book or watch TV because he spent all his time obsessing and agitated. I was very concerned for his future and for my mother's emotional state because of all the stress my father's situation put on her.

One fateful day

Then one fateful day I met a psychiatrist at a social gathering. I didn't suspect at the time that meeting him would change the course of my life, my father's life, and eventually the lives of many others who would become my clients, but it did.

This psychiatrist encouraged me to investigate neurofeedback. I had never heard of it. Although he suggested it could be effective in helping people with brain-based issues like depression and anxiety, I remained skeptical: if it was so good, why hadn't I heard about it? (Little did I know I'd hear this question repeatedly once I got involved in the field).

Putting skepticism aside

Skepticism aside, I was desperate to find a solution for my dad. Since only limited research was on the internet at the time, I couldn't just "Google it," so I ordered research papers from Emory University's library. I also called a half-dozen psychologists and medical doctors around the country who were using neurofeedback. Amazingly, all of them ended up taking my calls and assured me that it did, in fact, work. The concepts made sense to me. I wondered, "Could this help my dad?"

A surprising success

We had already tried everything else: what did we have to lose? Hopeful that this new technology could help my father, I located an experienced neurofeedback clinician two hours outside of Atlanta and six hours from my parents' home in Tennessee. We arranged for my dad to undergo intensive neurofeedback training twice a day for ten days. On the sixth day, when I walked into his training room at the neurofeedback center, he looked up and said, "Hi, Mike. How are you doing?" That sure was different! Prior to that, my father couldn't even engage in a simple exchange that most of us take for granted. Even better, this dramatic change in him occurred in a very short time.

I wondered how the heck neurofeedback could have helped him when the best doctors had failed to reach him and find a solution to his problems. Witnessing its positive impact on my father was enough to intrigue and motivate me.

It took many more training sessions and other therapies for him to get better and break out of his problem, but neurofeedback clearly made a significant impact in helping him regain a good part of his life until his death in 2010.

Discovering my passion

Impressed, I was amazed that neurofeedback didn't have more visibility. I thought I'd try to help spread the word to more people in my free time, on behalf of my dad's neurofeedback provider.

I offered to organize a lecture at Clemson University in South Carolina, near my dad's provider at the time. We also enlisted the help of the psychiatrist who recommended neurofeedback to me. The talk was about an alternative to medications for mental health issues. It was mentioned briefly in the local paper and on the radio. *One-hundred twenty-five people showed up!* I was really surprised. Many attendees expressed their frustration with medications that either didn't work or didn't help enough. They didn't know what else to do or where to go.

Crazy to leave high tech while it was really booming?

The response to the lecture prompted me to give up my high-paying career in the soaring technology field. I decided to dive into a new career in neurofeedback. In 1996 I opened a clinic in Atlanta with the neurofeedback practitioner who helped my dad.

Why did I take a chance on neurofeedback when I already had a career? I wanted to help people, and there were (and still are) so many people who need help with their brain. Frankly, neuroplasticity and the technology intrigued the heck out of me. What it did for my dad and a few other people I met was amazing, yet virtually no one knew about it. That challenge appealed to me, and I thought I could help educate people. In retrospect, educating people has been a never-ending challenge, but the field has come a long way.

Learning and teaching

During my first 18 months I was able to take numerous neurofeedback courses. I worked out an arrangement to attend courses around the country by helping support and teach the technology to health care professionals. In those days, technology was more complex and a bigger obstacle to learning neurofeedback than it is today (though it's still a factor). Since then, I've helped several thousand providers learn neurofeedback.

I've had the privilege of being educated by the best people in the field, including many of its pioneers. I've learned the most from teaching courses to clinicians, and from the clients at our center who share with me daily how their brain responds to neurofeedback. It's through that feedback that I've continued to learn about adapting to each individual's unique response to brain training.

PART 1

What is Neurofeedback
and How does it Work?

Let's begin with the first question most people have:

Does neurofeedback really work?

Yes. *Experienced providers report significant improvements between 70-85 percent of the time* among clients who train regularly and for as long as their situation requires. This is consistent with published research. That being said, there are caveats which we explain later, when things don't go as well, or when people quit training prematurely.

CHAPTER ONE

Brain Basics

How can neurofeedback help me "improve" my brain? To understand, it helps to talk about how the different areas of the brain play different roles.

I'll start with an exercise analogy. Let's say my left arm is very weak. It's so weak I can barely lift a bottle of water to drink it.

Someone tells me that to make my arm stronger I can tense my arm muscles 100 times a day, so I practice that. The first day, my arm doesn't feel stronger. It may even feel weaker and tired. But after tensing my muscles daily, my arm eventually gets stronger. Almost everyone can get stronger from exercise (though some take longer than others) and that's similar to how neurofeedback works.

Imagine I have "weak" temporal lobes in my brain (there's one on each side of your head). The temporal lobes play a role in helping manage emotions. Think of temporal lobes as a circuit. That circuit plays a role when you get excessively emotionally triggered, anxious or upset. When that circuit is stronger—or functioning more efficiently—it helps you manage emotions better.

Who knew you could get better at controlling emotions by exercising your temporal lobes until they are "stronger" or firing more efficiently? That's where neurofeedback equipment comes in. You can feel your muscles, but you can't feel neurons firing in your brain.

The technology tells your brain instantly when your neurons are doing their job better—being more efficient—and when they're not.

For example, you'll hear a beep when your brain has an appropriate level of activity but will hear no beep when part of your brain is too active or not active enough. If the neurofeedback involves showing a movie, the movie will fade out or get smaller when your brain is not firing efficiently. You see the movie more clearly when your circuit is firing better.

Your brain *learns* to do better from the feedback. We'll explain this in detail later.

*Our brain learns from
repeated practice and feedback.*

Roles of Parts of the Brain

The more you know about the brain, the easier it is to understand neurofeedback. Here are a few examples of the roles that different areas of the brain play as they relate to neurofeedback. This explanation is overly simplified, and there is much more to know. However, for purposes of this book, it provides a basic overview.

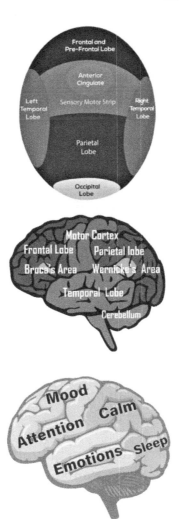

Temporal lobes

A high percentage of children and adults who train their temporal lobe activity with neurofeedback report managing their emotions better. The number of sessions to achieve that improvement can vary greatly by individual. Everyone is unique, so each individual's training may be somewhat different (you'll notice this theme throughout the book).

Training the left temporal lobe tends to impact anger, irritation, depression, self-esteem and emotional resilience. It also plays a role in language, such as how we find words, and in auditory processing. The right temporal lobe impacts anxiety, including social anxiety and other functions.

EXAMPLE: Temporal lobe training on a 10-year-old with emotional outbursts.

We worked with a 10-year-old boy who was about to be thrown out of his fourth school because of emotional outbursts. When he came to us, he was taking medication that was supposed to calm him. However, he was still dealing with agitation, anger and sleep problems. By the end of his fifth 30-minute session over a three-week period, he had become much calmer, had gained better control of himself and was permitted to remain in school.

We didn't teach this young man anything about emotional control. We just helped him exercise the EEG patterns in his temporal lobes to make that part of his brain work better. Improved functioning in his temporal lobes allowed him to better manage his frustration and temper.

Reinforcement of new brain patterns was essential to producing permanent, long-term benefits. Once he completed about 15 more sessions, the boy more consistently managed his behavior, even while his physician lowered his medications.

Frontal/pre-frontal lobes

The frontal lobe is important in mood, motivation and attention. It can play a role as a control center for emotions and for self-control. The pre-frontal lobe affects issues such as managing attention, organizing, planning, decision-making, staying on task, short-term memory and impulse control. Together they are often associated with ADD/ADHD, short-term memory and executive function issues.

Anterior cingulate

Issues in this "frontal midline" area often relate to being "stuck," having difficulty transitioning, and tendencies to an obsessive or racing mind. It plays an important role in shifting into and out of "overwhelm." It also affects the flexibility of attention.

Parietal lobe

The parietal lobe can affect sensory integration and contribute to being overwhelmed with too much stimulation or information. Difficulty with "overwhelm" often looks like anxiety. This area can affect processing speed, thereby impacting school, work and life. The parietal lobe can also play a role in feeling safe in your body and experiencing a greater sense of self. It is often used in training clients with anxiety and PTSD (post-traumatic stress disorder).

Occipital lobe

The occipital lobe plays a role in visual processing. It can impact reading, sports performance (such as catching or hitting a ball), light sensitivity, tracking movement and much more.

Motor cortex

The motor cortex influences coordination, gross and fine motor skills and the acquisition and performance of skilled movement. It contributes to how good you are at sports.

When trained with neurofeedback, it plays a role in modulating alert and awake states (generalized arousal).

A 13-year-old boy with processing issues and developmental delays loved baseball and wanted to play well like his older brother did. He was too slow to be effective at hitting and catching. However, after about 10 neurofeedback training sessions over the motor cortex, he (and his father) was thrilled with his improvements both in speed and ability to play baseball. With more training he continued to improve.

CHAPTER TWO

Four Principles of Neurofeedback... Who and How it Helps

How can neurofeedback help you with the brain-related symptoms you're dealing with? Let's start with what I consider to be four basic principles of neurofeedback:

1. Anyone can quickly learn to change their brain pattern using neurofeedback.

2. Changing your brain pattern can improve how your brain functions, often in profound ways.

3. Neurofeedback training is simple to do, but how and why it works can be difficult to understand.

4. <u>Neurofeedback doesn't do anything to your brain</u>. It provides feedback to help your brain learn how to change its firing pattern (re-wire itself).

In simplest terms, neurofeedback technology measures a specified brain pattern at a particular site or area. In some situations, you want your brain to make *more* of a certain pattern. In other situations, you want your brain to make *less* of a certain pattern. In both cases, the neurofeedback equipment instantly gives you feedback whenever your brain accomplishes your particular goal.

We will discuss this further in Chapter Six: The Power of Patterns.

Neurofeedback uses sound, visuals and vibration for feedback

Feedback includes sounds like beeps, music and vibrations. Typical visuals are a Pac-Man type game, rockets, race cars and movies fading in and out. It can even involve tactile vibrating pads or stuffed animals. There are many options.

To do neurofeedback training you don't have to do anything specific...just listen or watch. Even if you're not paying attention, your brain seems to make sense of the feedback, and responds.

You're not training symptoms

Neurofeedback training doesn't directly target symptoms, nor does it resolve all issues. Neurofeedback simply assists you in improving your brain timing—which in turn helps improve brain function or symptoms. It's exercise that helps your brain "do better" or be more efficient.

Neurofeedback is like "heavy-duty weight training" for the brain. It allows you to target and strengthen key brain circuits with real-time feedback.

You've tried everything else

It's remarkable how many people struggle with issues even after seeing numerous top health care professionals. Many who find neurofeedback say they've tried numerous conventional and alternative treatments that didn't work very well.

Others come because they don't want to be on medication. And there are those who come who don't believe in neurofeedback but are encouraged (or dragged) to try it by a loved one.

Here's a case in point: A male client told me that a close female friend had pushed him to try neurofeedback for his chronic anger issues. "I thought it was a bunch of bull, but since nothing else had worked I figured it wouldn't hurt and would at least satisfy her," he remarked. Twenty-five sessions later he was surprised at the improvement in his anger problem. Friends and co-workers commented how much he had changed, too. "I'm not getting all pissed off anymore," he tol d me. "It's remarkable. I didn't expect that kind of life-changing effect — with a bunch of beeps."

Who can be helped?

I'm frequently asked, "Who can benefit from neurofeedback?" The answer is "almost everyone" (if they're interested in being helped).

Neurofeedback is nothing more than a powerful tool for brain workouts. Because neurofeedback in essence "builds up" or strengthens key brain patterns, it improves cortical timing and communication. Better timing enables different areas of your brain to perform more efficiently.

Even if you're not suffering from a specific condition, a more efficient brain helps you with day-to-day issues. Here's a partial list of situations that respond well to neurofeedback:

- School, work and sports performance
- Organizational ability
- Self-expression
- Quality and speed of decision-making
- Ability to handle stress
- Social interactions
- Relationships
- Staying sharp as you age
- Emotional resilience

Brain challenges that are particularly responsive to neurofeedback include:

- ADHD, kids struggling in school or at home
- Depression and anxiety
- Poor sleep—difficulty falling asleep, staying asleep, or early awakening
- A racing mind or getting "stuck" in thoughts
- Obsessive thinking or behavior
- Difficulty managing emotions (outbursts, crying, anger)
- Being easily frustrated or triggered
- Processing/cognitive issues or learning disabilities (being a "slow learner"): these manifest as struggles in school with reading (dyslexia), writing and math.
- Language and expression: writing or verbalizing is harder or slower than it should be
- Developmental delays/autistic spectrum disorders
- Chronic migraines or headaches
- Neurological issues like concussions, TBI, or seizures
- PTSD, nightmares
- Panic attacks
- Sensory processing disorders, fine and gross motor skills
- Developmental Trauma/Attachment

CASE EXAMPLE: I trained a bright 22-year-old woman who had suffered from high anxiety since childhood. Despite years of anti-anxiety medications, CBD oil and pot, she remained anxious, easily overwhelmed and triggered. After the first session, she observed that she felt much calmer. Over three months, she completed nine sessions with us before leaving the area to attend graduate school. A while later, we received a note from her saying, "… my visits there were life-changing. I am in a healthier, happier place than I've ever been before thanks to my time there."

Given the scope and complexity of her problem, I expected it to take far longer than nine sessions to have a significant impact. Because we didn't see her after that, I don't know if some or all her improvements stuck beyond the two months we stayed in contact. Only time can tell. Before she left, I suggested she complete more training sessions for reinforcement at her school, but she may have learned enough to maintain a significant improvement without them.

As part of our integrative approach, we suggested she take specific supplements in addition to the neurofeedback training, which may also have contributed to her success.

Note: We inform our clients that nutrition, supplements and gut health can play a role in helping them improve, because these affect the brain as well as the body. Neurofeedback often works without these changes, but I'd argue that proper diet and high-quality supplements can often speed up training progress. See the Appendix for more information.

CHAPTER THREE

A Simple Explanation of Neurofeedback

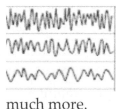 You can't feel your brainwaves, but they're active all the time. They play a vital role in how you think, pay attention, manage your moods, sleep, process information—and so much more.

If you struggle with "brain symptoms," training key brain-wave patterns to work more efficiently can help you feel calmer, reduce anxiety, facilitate restful sleep and improve your mood,  among many other things. But how do you do it?

Neurofeedback technology gives you a window into your brainwave patterns (and other measures).

Sensors are placed on your head and typically are connected to a device such as an EEG amplifier or computer.

This neurofeedback technology tells you INSTANTLY when your brain makes more or less of certain brain patterns (this is called real-time feedback).

How does it tell you what your brain is doing?

Three examples

1. As you watch a movie, you see it more clearly when your brain fires in the desired pattern. When your brain does NOT fire in the desired pattern, the movie fades out (or gets smaller). This is your feedback.

Brain engaged   **Brain Disengaged**

2. With another program, a Pac-Man will stop or go, depending on how much activity your brain is making. You'll also hear beeps, or the beeps will stop.

3. In other programs you'll hear a sound change the instant your brain pattern changes.

These are just three examples. There are many games, visuals and sounds that can be employed to accomplish the same goal.

Try changing your brain pattern

Let's try a little experiment: Concentrate as hard as you can on your right temporal lobe (above the right ear). Try to increase the number of neurons firing 12 to 15 times per second over that part of your brain.

Did you do it? Of course not. You can't feel your neurons, nor can you change how your neurons are firing just by thinking about them. With the neurofeedback tool, however, you *can* do it.

Neurofeedback tells your brain what it's doing

Early biofeedback experiments showed that people could learn to slow their heartbeat or change the temperature of their skin by watching a monitor (biofeedback) of that activity. It's the same principle with the brain.

Neurofeedback alerts you in real time when your brain makes more of the desired pattern. It uses "rewards" like sounds or interesting visuals to tell your brain when it's making more or less of the target pattern being measured. Being able to see or hear this activity helps you to effortlessly—and often without awareness—increase or decrease the activity being monitored. Your brain responds to the feedback.

It doesn't matter whether the feedback involves watching a Pac-Man or a movie, piloting a rocket ship or changing a sound. The principle is the same.

The cool part? Your brain does the rest.

The big deal here is that for the most part, your brain does the work for you.

As your brain receives feedback that it's producing a desired pattern, it typically starts making more of that pattern. Automatically.

This process resembles the way you learn a song without trying or even paying attention. Have you ever caught yourself humming or singing a new song when you didn't make any conscious effort to learn that song?

How did that happen?

Your brain picked up and learned the song's pattern. The brain is, in essence, a pattern-learning machine. Neurofeedback takes advantage of this and helps the brain practice reinforcing or changing key patterns.

Take the case of someone who suffers from anxiety. Their neurofeedback goal could be to produce more of a calm brain pattern. The brain hears or sees the feedback (visual or auditory) and starts "tapping along" automatically, trying to make more of that calm pattern. With practice, you get much better at it.

What's important for the provider is picking the right brain patterns to reinforce (train). In addition, not everyone responds the same way. Carefully observing the impact of training helps the provider make any necessary adjustments. Sometimes the impact of training is obvious. Sometimes it's subtle and takes longer or is harder to notice. In theory, neurofeedback professionals should help guide you through this process.

Watching your brain change itself

We've talked about how your brain can automatically learn and respond using feedback. With neurofeedback, you can watch yourself figure out how to change your brain patterns — all without knowing how.

Kids don't care about the "how." If you ask a child, "Can you play a game with your brain?" most say yes and are ready to do it — or think it's kind of cool. Many adults, on the other hand, are more hesitant. They want to know "how do I do it?" and ask lots of other "how" questions. I usually suggest they just watch the screen or listen to the sound — you don't really have to do anything else. *Your brain will figure it out.*

Here are three examples of neurofeedback exercises.

1. You see three spaceships. The one in the middle needs to fly ahead. The one on the right and left need to stay back. In this example the ship on the right is too far ahead. Your job is to guide it back and keep the middle ship in front. Each ship moves in response to your brain pattern. It's not the computer that controls the ships — it's your brain. Your brain gradually figures it out. It's remarkable how quickly kids and adults improve at this activity. When you succeed — and you will — you are changing your brain pattern.

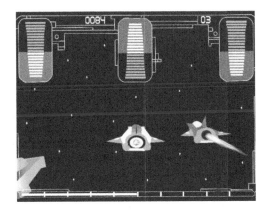

2. You're asked to watch your EEG (below). Your goal is to make fewer tall waves and more short waves. For example, try to decrease the Average below (64.2 microvolts) down to 50 microvolts. The smaller the waves, the smaller the microvolts. So how do you do it? If you focus on the waves and "want them" to get smaller, your brain typically will figure out how. In fact, most children and adults can learn to lower the number and size of the waves fairly rapidly. When I ask how they changed it, some can describe the process but others have no idea how they did it. Since you can't feel your brainwaves, you can't feel them change. Lowering the average means, in essence, you're training neurons in your brain to be more efficient in how they fire—and function.

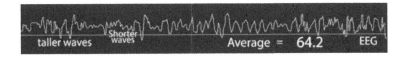

3. The bars in the graph below jump up and down, changing every half second. Your instructions are to

make the bars jump less and to make them shorter. Doing so helps neurons in your brain fire more efficiently (as in example 2 above).

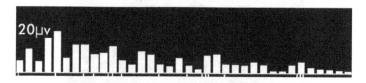

Many people are surprised that they can start making changes to the pattern within 30-90 seconds. If you ask them how they did it, they usually say they have no clue. Even when they succeed, some people insist they didn't do anything. Typical of neurofeedback, if you just watch, your brain usually figures it out.

How can you do neurofeedback without understanding it? My best explanation is this: If I instructed you to raise your arm above your head, you can do it, but you can't tell me exactly how you did it. You didn't "think your arm up." You didn't think about moving the muscles. It was done unconsciously. You wanted it to go up, so your brain figured out how. It's similar in neurofeedback. You "intend" your brain to make changes, and it figures it out.

Note: The bars in the illustration above represent EEG activity in your brain. Each bar shows groups of neurons firing at different speeds. The higher the bar, the more groups of neurons there are that are firing together. Often, you want all the bars to be smaller, which tends to represent a more efficient pattern. This graph is called a spectral display and is a common feature of neurofeedback systems.

Read more about patterns in Chapter Six.

More detail about how neurofeedback works (if you want)

Every neuron is connected to up to 10,000 other neurons in vast networks that crisscross the brain. Changes in one area of the brain can cause reverberations throughout other areas.

Here's an example: Many people can improve mood and energy by training more neurons to fire 15-18 times per second (the beta frequency) over the left frontal part of the brain. (Note there are other ways to train mood and energy—this is just an example).

To encourage that pattern, one sensor is placed over the left frontal/central part of the head and another on the left ear. The client watches a game on a computer screen (say a Pac-Man type game). Any time beta activity increases, there's a beep, and the Pac-Man eats a dot. When there is less beta wave activity, the Pac-Man slows down.

Your brain figures out the game and gets better at it, without your awareness. In this case, increased beta helps a certain percentage of people feel more energized or alert (almost like drinking coffee).

Brain timing: If too many neurons in your brain are firing faster, or more slowly than they should be, or aren't passing messages to other neurons quickly enough, it will impact how well your brain functions.

Neurofeedback appears to help change the firing rate and messaging of neurons across brain networks.

Advanced topic: Disruption or "re-routing"— a different point of view?

There are times when one or two short neurofeedback events (a few minutes or less) can produce a profound change. How could such a short amount of learning produce such a big change? Because the brain can learn and adapt in a matter of seconds.

Imagine someone criticizing you ("You are stupid") or complimenting you ("You are amazing") in front of a crowd of 300 people. Many people would react strongly to this verbal feedback, even though it only took a second or two. This feedback could impact them for an hour, a day or a lifetime.

During those two seconds, the brain re-routed its neural functioning.

Isn't it therefore possible that the response to neurofeedback causes the brain to change its pattern and re-organize itself? In other words, rather than assume that the brain is simply learning a new pattern, could the feedback help disrupt and change old patterns as the brain reorganizes itself?

Over the years many neurofeedback providers have discussed the idea of disruption, and this is something I have observed. It appears that their brain is breaking well-established and less-than-optimal patterns.

CHAPTER FOUR

A Brief History of Neurofeedback

A good history of neurofeedback is contained in the book *A Symphony in the Brain* by Jim Robbins. You can read more history of biofeedback and neurofeedback published online in *Biofeedback* by Peper and Shaffer[2]. For the purpose of the book, here's a synopsis of a few key historic moments.

The initial neurofeedback research came from Dr. Joe Kamiya's work, starting in 1966[3] at the University of Chicago, and Dr. Barry Sterman's work at UCLA, starting in 1967.

Studying consciousness, Dr. Kamiya discovered[4] that if he gave feedback to people when their brain made alpha brainwaves (the waves prevalent during wakeful relaxation with closed eyes), some of them could learn to make more alpha. This was the first EEG neurofeedback training.

Along similar lines, Dr. Sterman published an experiment[5] showing that cats could increase one type of brain wave called sensory-motor rhythm (SMR). SMR is a brain state exhibited

---

[2] https://biofeedbackhealth. files.wordpress.com/2011/01/biofeedback-history-peper-shaffer.pdf
[3] https://www.ncbi.nlm.nih.gov/pmc/articles/PMC3424312/
[4] https://doi.org/10.1111/j.1469-8986.1970.tb01756.x
[5] https://www.sciencedirect.com/science/article/abs/pii/003193846890139X

during relaxation and stillness. They were rewarded with food every time they "got it right" and quickly learned to control their brainwaves to receive the treat.

NASA experiment with cats

Subsequently, NASA asked Dr. Sterman to conduct an experiment[6] to determine the effects of exposure to rocket fuel, concerned it was affecting workers and the astronauts. When he exposed cats to increasing levels of rocket fuel, most of the cats went into a seizure and died within an hour.

However, some of the cats took two hours or more to go into seizures. When they did, their seizures were less severe. He discovered that the cats that had been trained to increase SMR activity in the previous experiment had reduced seizures. In a published study, Dr. Sterman concluded that the SMR training played a role in inhibiting seizures in the cats. He moved on to train SMR in seizure patients, who were nonresponsive to medications, and published that data. Research by several other scientists who drew similar conclusions was subsequently published in peer-reviewed journals.

In 2006, Dr. Sterman, with Tobias Egner, published an analysis and rationale on neurofeedback[7], which reviewed numerous seizure studies. They published a follow-up in 2010[8]. Dr. Sterman observed that for 174 patients with uncontrolled seizures, 82 percent showed significantly improved seizure control. Additional research has been published in this area since.

---

[6] http://www.isnr-jnt.org/article/viewFile/16596/10560
[7] https://link.springer.com/article/10.1007%2Fs10484-006-9002-x
[8] https://www.ncbi.nlm.nih.gov/pubmed/20622079

However, without a major company to promote the technology behind those studies, neurologists remained for the most part unaware of this research.

Other researchers working with seizure patients quickly learned that training brain patterns made a positive, significant impact well beyond seizures. Over the years, neurofeedback came out of the labs and was applied increasingly to people with attention deficit (ADD/ADHD), led by the work of Dr. Joel Lubar[9]. It has expanded since then to cover many brain conditions including autism, anxiety, depression, migraines and a growing number of psychological and neurological-based conditions.

Even with the number of studies expanding, neurofeedback has struggled to become mainstream due to the lack of support from a major company. It is taught in only a small number of universities. However, it is becoming better known, as patients and health care practitioners seek alternative solutions to a myriad of problems.

Growing awareness of neurofeedback

The field of neurofeedback is slowly continuing to expand and gain more acceptance. Here are a few of the reasons, in my opinion.

1. Neurofeedback helps people with many clinical symptoms when other interventions have failed and often reduces reliance on medications. Word-of-mouth from patients to health care professionals is increasing aware-

---

[9] http://www.eegfeedback.org/publications.html

ness. Neurofeedback providers are reporting more referrals from medical and mental health professionals than ever.

2. There is a greater interest in non-medication interventions among the general population. Internet searches are leading many people to learn about and investigate neurofeedback.

3. There's more information available to the public about neurofeedback and neuroplasticity. They're being talked about in the media by prominent professionals such as psychiatrist Dr. Daniel Amen and Dr. Mehmet Oz. As people search the term "neuroplasticity," they're ending up on neurofeedback websites, since neurofeedback is a tool that engages neuroplasticity to change the brain's electrical patterns.

4. A growing number of studies, articles, books, published client cases, case studies, videos, news and online interviews with health professionals has increased the visibility and credibility of neurofeedback.

5. Some health insurance companies and health systems (in various countries) are providing reimbursement or partial coverage for neurofeedback. Many more are still denying it, but a gradual shift appears to be occurring.

6. A small but growing number of physicians, psychologists and mental health professionals—including psychiatrists and neurologists—offers neurofeedback to patients. This adds credibility to the field. Even a few hospitals around the world are offering it.

CHAPTER FIVE

Believe It or Not, You Really *Can* Change your Brain

Let's say you've spent years trying everything you've heard of to:

- Reduce or manage your anxiety or worry
- Help your child's struggles in school
- Control your migraines/panic attacks/seizures
- Improve sleep, attention, mood or processing
- Recover from a concussion

Yet none of the medications, therapies or other modalities have alleviated your problem—at least not consistently. Frustrated, you may start to believe, "That's just how I am. I have to live with this."

Well...no, you don't. Many people who visit me have difficulty believing they can change themselves after years or even decades of issues—just by training. Here's one example:

A 21-year-old client told me she'd suffered from anxiety for as long as she could remember. Although anxiety had interfered with her life and college plans, she accepted her "fate" and identified herself as a bundle of nerves, with no chance of being different.

After her fourth neurofeedback session, she noted she could calm herself better than she'd ever been able to before. She had to work hard to redefine who she was—someone who wasn't chronically anxious.

Her brain and nervous system had become very proficient at producing patterns (habits) that felt like ingrained anxiety. She had "perfected" being an anxious person. With neurofeedback training, she was able to alleviate those patterns. After additional sessions to create lasting benefits prior to going back to college, she told us that she no longer defined herself as an anxious person.

Where do you get help? Not where you thought.

Chances are, you or someone you know struggles with sleep issues…or anxiety…or depression…or ADHD…or hit their head and later started having more problems. I'm willing to bet no one ever suggested to "go down to the neurofeedback center and practice changing your brain pattern until the problem resolves." Neurofeedback simply isn't most people's first, or even second, resort.

Neurofeedback—a high-tech gym for the brain

I liken neurofeedback training to a high-tech gym for your brain, with some yoga thrown in. Clients who "work out their brain" with neurofeedback report being more emotionally balanced, mentally stable, flexible and resilient. It sounds a bit like the benefits of yoga but is more specific to brain function.

It takes time and patience

If your brain can learn to walk, ride a bicycle or make scrambled eggs, it can learn to function another way. It's no different from learning a new habit.

How long will it take? The most accurate answer is—there is no exact answer.

It's similar to…how long does it take to get in shape if I start working out at the gym? Or how long will it take to learn multiplication tables?

You change your own brain pattern by "working out." You just need the right equipment.

Your brain learns with PRACTICE, PRACTICE, PRACTICE

How do you learn multiplication tables? You review them (you practice) until your brain "gets" them. It takes repetition. Some people learn them quickly, others take longer.

How do you learn to ride a bike? You keep trying until you stop falling.

How do you learn to play the piano? You practice each element over and over until you don't have to think about it.

Everyone's different, and it's hard to predict, but practice helps you get better at any task. Stick with it, and you'll usually achieve your goals. With the help of neurofeedback, your brain has a **remarkable capacity to change itself** in a positive way.

The neurofeedback edge (over meds)

A major advantage of neurofeedback over medications is that once your brain learns new patterns, it tends to stick. Not always, but typically. (We'll talk about exceptions in Part 3, Frequently Asked Questions about Neurofeedback). On the other hand, when you stop taking your medications, you're likely to go back to where you started.

I mentioned this earlier, but it's important enough to repeat: **The technology doesn't change your brain. It only assists you in doing it *yourself*.** If you do enough neurofeedback training (repetition and practice), you're likely to experience improvement. How much training it takes for any individual to experience noticeable change varies. Over time your brain will get in better shape.

Changing brain patterns can have benefits, including improvements in:

- Sleep patterns
- Racing mind
- Mood
- Listening capacity
- Speech
- Speed of learning
- Sensory processing
- Chronic pain
- Migraines
- Neurological issues

- Emotional triggers

What sorts of quality of life improvements are common for people doing neurofeedback training?

- Less worry and anxiety
- More stable mood
- Less obsessing
- Better handling of stress
- Easier learning
- Better sleep
- Better ability to express yourself
- Better attention
- Improved relationships
- Fewer or less intense headaches
- Improved memory
- Better mental performance

Can anyone change their brain patterns by getting feedback?

For the most part, yes. Babies. Children. Adults. The elderly. As long as learning can occur, an individual can almost always respond to brain feedback.

How can neurofeedback possibly affect *all* these things?

There are circuits that play a role in attention, processing, managing mood, making decisions, language and memory — and far more. Improvement in any of these circuits can impact how well your brain performs.

When you improve brain circuits that affect sleep, you sleep better. When you target circuits that affect frustration tolerance or attention, those can improve…you get the idea.

You don't even have to pay attention

In my clinical experience spanning more than 20 years, children and adults often show symptom improvement with neurofeedback with ZERO awareness of how they train.

I will discuss this phenomenon of learning with patterns in Chapter Six.

Could certain patterns be trained faster or better by being aware? Probably. But many clients clearly respond to neurofeedback without any conscious awareness — just by getting feedback.

Here's one example:

A client in the middle of a bad migraine was brought to see me. He ranked his pain an 8.5 on a 10-point scale. Light and sound bothered him, so I turned the lights off and kept the volume of the beeps down so low they were barely perceptible. The client told me later that he ignored the beeping as much as possible.

After 20 minutes of training with his eyes closed, the man's migraine went from 8.5 to 2 on the pain scale. He reported that he had never experienced such quick relief. He said that even with medications it would normally take an entire day to fully calm down and recover.

Even though he wasn't paying attention to the feedback due to the pain, his brain responded to the feedback as it reinforced the pattern being measured. With no effort and no attention to the process, his headache mostly went away. Solving one bad migraine didn't mean he had resolved his problem. He needed more training (practice), but it showed him that his brain could learn to get rid of a migraine on its own. The machine didn't do it—he did.

Note: Not everyone with a migraine responds as well as he did, but most migraineurs receive significant benefit. My experience, the experience of other clinicians and reports in two published studies indicate that at least 80% of chronic migraines are reduced and sometimes eliminated with neurofeedback.

CHAPTER SIX

The Power of Patterns

I like to say that your brain "learns patterns for a living." After a very small amount of exposure, your brain can identify patterns. For example, when a child gets a new video game, there's no need for an instruction manual. The child just starts playing. His brain instantly begins to identify patterns to help score points. With practice, the child improves rapidly by zeroing in on what works and what doesn't.

This process is a type of trial-and-error learning. It's how a lot of learning occurs—without cognitive awareness of the task being learned. You get better over time.

How is learning a song similar to neurofeedback?

Let's say you're listening to the radio. You hear an advertising jingle several times. The jingle is annoying, so you pay *no* attention to it. In fact, you ignore it (you think).

Later you realize this jingle is playing in your head.

How did that happen? You weren't paying attention. You made no effort to learn it. You tried to ignore it, yet after three or four exposures, your brain learned the jingle's pattern automatically with no effort—and it's stuck in your head.

We often think that learning requires focus, which is true for certain types of learning, like multiplication tables. However, many other types of learning align with the jingle and video game examples. The brain is learning or responding to patterns.

Neurofeedback reinforces patterns

The computer provides instant feedback whenever your brain makes a specific pattern. Your brain will automatically start making more of the targeted pattern with no effort...or awareness ...or attention.

As the brain responds to the pattern, it becomes more efficient at making the pattern. This is learning, but without any attentional effort. Your brain in essence "taps along" to its own beat.

The BEEP, BEEP, BEEP.

How does your brain learn from a beep?

I'd like to illustrate pattern learning. I need your help to do this.

Imagine you're sitting in front of a computer screen. There are sensors on your head measuring a specific EEG pattern. You hear a beep each time your brain is making enough of the pattern being measured.

Say the next line out loud to yourself—or preferably to someone else.

Beep. Beep. Beep. Beep. Beep. Beep. Beep.
Be silent. for 3 seconds. . . . .
Say the next line out loud.
Beep. Beep. Beep. Beep.

Be silent for two seconds . . .

If you hear seven beeps in a row over four seconds, your brain has identified a pattern of beeps. The moment the beeps stopped, your brain said, "There were supposed to be more beeps."

The instant there was silence, it knew the beeps should keep going.

The brain will automatically and unconsciously try to fill in the gaps and make more beeps to keep the pattern going. It can't help itself.

YOUR BRAIN COMPLETES all kinds of patterns—automatically.

What does your brain do when you hear…?

"Mary had a little…"
"Twinkle, twinkle, little…"
"When the cat's away the mice will…"
"Melts in your mouth not in your…"
A B C D…

Your brain tries to complete those phrases (patterns) whether you intended to or not.

When doing neurofeedback, your brain identifies the feedback as a pattern. Whenever the pattern changes or is interrupted, the brain works to correct it and complete the pattern. As your brain hears the feedback, it "taps along" by making more of that activity.

EXAMPLE 1: Let's say you're very anxious. Learning to make more alpha brainwaves in the back of your head often has a calming effect. Neurofeedback gives you feedback (such as a beep or other sounds) whenever your brain makes a desired level of alpha. The beep stops when your brain isn't making enough alpha. Your brain will typically get better at increasing the number of beeps over time. It essentially taps along to its own beat (beep.)

EXAMPLE 2: Let's say that too many neurons in your left temporal lobe are firing slowly (four times per second). These excessive theta brainwaves can contribute to feeling irritable, being easily frustrated or even depressed. Neurofeedback can help you practice making less theta. It gives instant feedback whenever you successfully suppress that pattern. With practice, you would typically get better at suppressing or modulating the theta.

CHAPTER SEVEN

Judge Improvements by Trends— 3 Illustrative Trend Charts

When doing neurofeedback, it's best to judge improvement by trends, not by day-to-day impressions of how you're doing.

Those who stick with training usually succeed. Many of my clients make steady progress with neurofeedback. Some people have ups and downs along the way. Here are some observations about expectations of the process:

1. Don't expect to feel like you're better after every single neurofeedback session. Anticipate setbacks. Lots of factors beyond neurofeedback can interrupt progress.

2. Look for little changes, not big ones. Progress is frequently incremental.

3. It takes time and practice to gain resilience. When you learn a new skill or sport, you don't get good or consistent all at once. It's the same with neurofeedback. Stick with it.

4. Look for positive trends or fewer negative symptoms. For example: (a) fewer bad days; (b) symptoms that are

less intense or shorter; or (c) faster improvement than you'd expect, given your history.

5. Be patient, be patient, be patient. **Everyone learns at a different rate**. Give your brain time to rewire itself. In most cases, it can get there.

Note: Not everyone who tries neurofeedback succeeds. When it's taking too long to establish a clear trend from training, I work with the client to identify issues that may be interfering with progress or discuss other options the client can pursue. These issues are discussed more in Part 3 (Frequently Asked Questions about Neurofeedback).

To illustrate how improvement occurs over time, I've put together "trend line" graphs below that represent the experiences of three clients.

Each dot represents a neurofeedback session, typically once or twice per week. Dots above the line indicate sessions that resulted in improvement. Dots below the line indicate sessions that had a setback.

Example 1: This client was "easy" and made steady progress. However, even this fairly uncomplicated client had some days when she felt better than others.

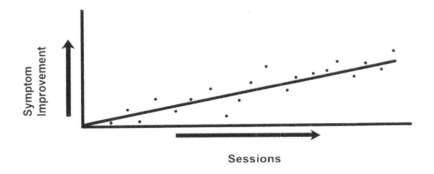

Example 2: This client's situation was more complex. He required more sessions to experience sustained improvement than the client in Example 1. Note that he had quite a few setbacks, but because he stuck with it, his improvement continued to trend upward.

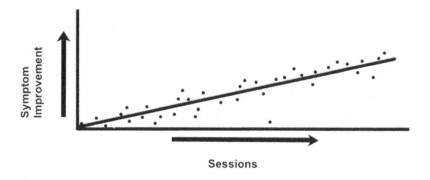

Example 3: This client had a long and complicated history of problems and medications. Notice that there are more ups and downs during his training vs. previous cases. His progress even trended downward at one point. I helped him identify several triggers he was unaware of (diet, environment). He almost quit, saying maybe neurofeedback wouldn't work for him. I kept reminding him that even with a dip, he was better than when he started—and he was. He persisted, and the progress continued to build.

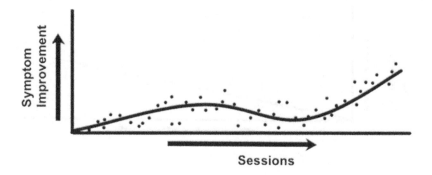

CHAPTER EIGHT

In-Depth Concepts for the Next Level of Understanding

Neurofeedback doesn't teach you skills such as:

a) how to calm yourself
b) how to behave around others
c) spelling
d) solving math problems

Instead, it helps you train the circuits of your brain to do a better job of calming, having self-control, spelling, or solving a math problem. I think of it as training to improve brain circuit efficiency. When the circuits that play a role in those tasks work better, you do better.

Where and how to train—a complicated question

It would be fantastic if one spot on the head correlated to anxiety or ADHD or depression or worry, but the brain is FAR MORE COMPLEX than that. Everyone's brain is unique. Two people with the same symptoms may respond differently to training on the same spot. That's why it's critical to adapt training for the needs of each individual. This is where your practitioner's level of training or experience can be important.

Providers have at their disposal a variety of models and tools for determining the appropriate type of neurofeedback training, as well as where and how to train. These include relating symptoms to specific areas of the brain, EEG analysis, adapting training to fit an EEG and using a variety of qEEG (quantitative EEG) brain maps. Personally, I don't think there's one right way, although there are many who would disagree with me. I could write an entire book discussing the various approaches to neurofeedback. Section 3 (Frequently Asked Questions about Neurofeedback) includes a short discussion of this topic.

Consider these complicating concepts for training your brain:

Training different areas of the brain produces different outcomes.

Training the left prefrontal lobe creates a different effect or response than training over the right temporal lobe or the left parietal lobe. No matter where you train on the head, the feedback looks and sounds the same, but it's not the same training. The brain responds differently to feedback coming from different locations.

Training a different pattern in the same spot produces a different outcome.

Train two different frequencies in the same area of the brain, and you will have two different training effects.

Training the same pattern in two people can produce a different outcome.

Train two people with the same frequency (for example alpha) at the same site, and they may experience a completely different training effect.

That said, there are some common training protocols that initially have similar effects for 60-75% of people. How the remainder will respond to a standard training protocol is harder to predict. After training the same pattern several times, someone may start to respond differently. That could require an adjustment in the training protocol.

Neurofeedback can sometimes have an unintended outcome

The goal of neurofeedback is to train patterns that improve attention, anxiety, sleep, cognition and other brain issues. On occasion, someone who trained may instead feel a bit "off." Training can bring things to the surface and expose other issues. A client might report increased annoyance, irritability or more difficulty falling asleep, for example. The effects of a single training session are almost always short-lived. Not unlike an exercise workout, you may be "sore" (off) for one or two days, and then that feeling goes away. (There's further discussion of this in Part 3 Frequently Asked Questions about Neurofeedback.)

At the next brain workout, you can either adjust the exercise (make it shorter for example) or change the exercise. A well-trained provider will know how to adapt training to each individual's response and when to stick with the training to give it a chance to settle in.

Note: Remember, the equipment is only providing feed-back. How your brain responds to the feedback is what's important. It's your practitioner's job to adapt or coach you through the process until your response to neurofeedback works for you.

PART 2

Discussion of Case Examples

Reading research and textbooks helps you understand aspects of neurofeedback such as the science behind it, qEEG brain mapping, and how to use knowledge about brain function to better target the training.

However, reviewing cases seems to provide the most insight into the implications of brain training. In my experience, this holds true for both professionals and health consumers. Cases help you rapidly understand the impact of neurofeedback on people's lives, and how the principles apply.

Even after all these years, I am still impressed by the power of neurofeedback to get people's brains "on track," to help them break patterns and to self-regulate.

Below is a sampling of cases from our center. I do not represent these cases as research, but they are a powerful way to learn. I've selected these not because they're unusual but because they are *usual*—typical of responses we see. Colleagues report similar types of outcomes. I ruled out cases where neurofeedback was not the clear influencer of the change.

Keep in mind that (1) the number of sessions it takes to experience change varies immensely by individual and; (2) the response to a small number of sessions may only last for a short time. Though a small number of sessions usually will not resolve the problem, it shows what is possible. In some cases, a small number of sessions can make a major difference. It's impossible to predict from one individual to another.

Different approaches to neurofeedback

In my office, I work with a variety of neurofeedback systems and models. In some of the cases discussed, I include information about the general approach I took in training the client.

Not all providers use the same approaches that I do, but many report similar results. I believe there's no one "right way" for your brain to learn. I discuss the "different approaches" issue in Part 3.

Anxious teen

A mother brought in her 16-year-old daughter for help with extreme anxiety. She barely communicated with her mother. Due to the severity of her anxiety, she often stayed away from school, had difficulty making friends and eventually withdrew from high school to be home-schooled. She didn't want to come for neurofeedback training.

Before the mom would consider a qEEG brain map, she wanted to see if she could get her daughter to come consistently. We chose a protocol that works in a high percentage of cases with extremely anxious people. However, after five sessions, we saw very little progress, and the girl was still fighting her mother about coming. A complicating factor was that she was on the stimulant Adderall. I suspected that the med might be contributing to her anxiety.

Her mom began to wonder out loud if neurofeedback was going to help her daughter. I knew it eventually would, once I came up with the right protocol, but I had to do it quickly or she might stop coming. Once again I suggested a map, and this time her mother agreed.

I adjusted her training protocols using information from the qEEG map. It worked. Within two to three sessions her mom felt things were better. Her daughter quit fighting her about coming for training, and from that point on, she made steady, gradual improvements.

After about 10 more neurofeedback sessions the girl, who had extremely poor self-awareness and self-insight, was able to report that she was feeling better and less stressed. She started having meaningful conversations with my staff, her mother and me. She was able to go places more easily with much less anxiety, even to visit the school. She still needed additional training to help her, but her progress was significant.

Gruff dad softens up

I saw a 57-year-old man who was described by his wife as a "gruff bear type." He had challenges relating to her and their eight-year-old son. He was easily annoyed with his son when he wanted to play and often had limited patience with his demands. There was a tendency for him to be short with both his wife and his son.

After his first neurofeedback session, his wife told me that, for a couple of days afterward, his behavior was remarkably warmer toward her and their son.

After training over a three-to-four-month period, she reported that he was treating them with more openness and affection. His sense of humor from early in their marriage returned. He would even jump into the pool and play with his son.

His wife described him as being "like a new husband." However, when I asked her husband if he had noticed ANY change, he said: "No—I'm exactly the same." It was clear to his wife that his interactions with his family had transformed. (By the way, it's not unusual for people who train with neurofeedback to be unaware of changes.)

He has needed periodic maintenance to keep up with his gains. A reminder: if your brain does better for several days or longer and then can't hold the gain, it may be something other than neurofeedback keeping it from holding. Many factors can affect brain function and stability.

ADD student's attitude and grades improve

A woman brought her 15-year-old son to train for ADD. His grades had steadily dropped over the school year, and he was making C's, D's and F's. He disliked coming to our office and said it was a waste of his time. He also said he didn't have a problem.

When he arrived for his eighth weekly session, I asked his mother if she had seen any improvement. She said she didn't think neurofeedback was helping at all. When I inquired about his grades, she responded, "Oh, he's been making A's and B's in the last four to five weeks." After pointing out this shift, she realized it had occurred since he had been training. When I asked the boy if he realized that his grades had improved significantly in recent weeks, he responded yes, but that neurofeedback had nothing to do with it. He responded, "I just decided I wanted to make better grades."

This lack of awareness of slow subtle changes from training is common.

ADHD and too easily frustrated

Eleven-year-old John was a sensitive, emotional kid who could not handle frustration. His parents initially brought him in for ADHD and frequent meltdowns. He had been on stimulant medication for attention, but his parents took him off. They were concerned about side effects, including the possibility that the medication was stunting his growth.

He would cry and fall apart when things didn't go his way, including at baseball practice. This didn't go over well with his peers or his coach and caused significant stress on his parents.

During his first 18 sessions, we trained the temporal lobes to target emotions. After eight or nine sessions, he was having fewer meltdowns and emotional outbursts, but his improvements didn't hold consistently. Then his parents pushed me to start targeting his attention symptoms. Every time I did, he became more emotional. I finally told his parents we'd get the emotions under control before doing any more attention training. That strategy worked.

After about 30 sessions, he was more consistent at managing his emotions. He no longer fell apart with frustration. He was much easier to manage at home, at school and at baseball practice. He clearly had gained more self-control, and his parents felt far less stressed.

We were then able to train attention, which no longer affected his emotions. We also suggested the mom focus on his diet and nutrition. She reported she thought that helped.

He completed about 60 sessions over the course of a year. He was able eventually to get off his stimulant medications, pay attention at school, finish his daily homework and keep his grades up. About two-thirds of the way through, his parents started giving him caffeine before school. That, plus the neurofeedback, helped him perform well consistently without medication. We tracked him months out, and he was still doing very well.

Why was this boy's case complicated? One possible reason was that he had fallen and hit the front of his head hard at age seven. An MRI indicated no problem—but an MRI isn't a valid measure of concussion. Years later, our EEG brain map revealed the presence of large, slow brainwaves over his right eyebrow compared to other parts of his head. That often correlates with attention problems. It suggested the possibility that his fall at age seven had resulted in a low-level concussion that contributed to his later problems.

ADD student discovered he wasn't stupid

A 29-year-old man had spent most of the first 24 years of his life thinking he was stupid or, at the very least, had a severe case of attention deficit disorder (ADD).

From the earliest days, school was a nightmare. He was held back to repeat kindergarten. Diagnosed with ADD that same year, his doctor prescribed Ritalin (he would take some sort of stimulant all the way through his school career and beyond). Then his school placed him in special classes for slow learners. He was bullied by the other kids and called "stupid" and other names. Throughout his school career he had tutors. When he received his high school diploma, he had a "D" average. College was out. The career he hoped for was out. He had low self-confidence.

At our center, we did a qEEG connectivity brain map. It indicated problems associated with significant learning disabilities. It also identified patterns associated with attentional problems, though that didn't seem nearly as significant. Connectivity training targeted findings from the map, which I've found very helpful with learning disabilities.

The client did so well during the first three months of neurofeedback training that he was able to work with his physician to discontinue his stimulant medication and reduce his mood medication.

More importantly, he reported some major benefits. Within three sessions, he noticed he could read a map for the first time (visual/spatial processing improvement). He was able to write a check quickly, something that had been difficult for him because the lines on the check didn't make sense to his brain (visual processing). His chronic anxiety dramatically diminished. It was a big shift. I wondered how much of his anxiety was from being overwhelmed all the time.

It took another three months of training for him to improve his mood, his confidence and emotional resilience, and to feel more confident in his ability to learn. He started reading books that he couldn't tackle before. His reading comprehension level increased significantly. He said he was disappointed that he spent nearly 30 years of his life struggling unnecessarily. He's continued to do sessions periodically, which have resulted in continuing gains.

11-year old gets a chance for a more normal life (ADHD, speech, sleep, processing issues)

This 11-year-old boy came into the world with several strikes against him. His birth mother abused drugs while pregnant, and she lost parental rights not long after he was born. He was adopted at the age of 10 months.

He was a very "hyper" baby, but his new parents figured he was just energetic. However, when he began to speak, his language was significantly delayed. His earliest diagnosis was "anxiety," but his parents suspected it was more than that.

He eventually received numerous diagnoses, including a sensory processing disorder, phonological dyslexia (an extreme form of dyslexia), dysgraphia (difficulty writing), ADHD and profoundly delayed fine motor skills. He had meltdowns in school and at home.

He had severe sleep problems. Unable to sleep at night, he would nod off in school. A sleep study revealed he had an alarming deficit of REM sleep. Already taking medication for ADHD, his parents brought him to see us, seeking a viable alternative. (Underlying sleep disorders can contribute to many different problems for children.[10]) Our initial neurofeedback training focused on utilizing some common sleep training protocols. Within a few sessions, his sleeping (and waking) habits improved. His meltdowns reduced almost to zero. A follow-up sleep study conducted several months later indicated that his sleep patterns and REM sleep were completely normal.

After a year and a half of regular neurofeedback training, gradual but significant changes continued to occur. He began

---

[10] https://www.ncbi.nlm.nih.gov/pubmed/30927228

speaking better. Homework time went from a two-hour nightly battle with lots of yelling to calmly completing his assignments in 45 minutes every night. Additionally, his ADHD medication was reduced by 30 percent.

Boy's meltdown minimized

We trained a six-year-old boy who had numerous, extreme meltdowns. Over the first 11 sessions, there were periods when he clearly had fewer and shorter meltdowns. At other times, he reverted to his normal meltdown pattern. (Ups and downs are not uncommon. It can take time before a person's brain stabilizes from training. For more about this, see Chapter Seven: Judge Improvements by Trends.)

At his 12th session, I adjusted his training to see if we could speed up his progress. I anticipated he might have an exaggerated response because he had historically been highly sensitive to small changes in training. I instructed his mom to call my cell if that occurred.

She called early the next morning to tell me that he was having a full-blown, angry meltdown and didn't think she could get him to school. I suggested she bring him straight to my office. When they arrived, and per his mother's request, I picked him up mid-meltdown, carried him to our training room and placed him on her lap. She held him tight as he screamed, thrashed and tried to kick her and butt heads with her. Believe me, placing the sensors on his head was no easy feat.

I adjusted his training based on what I learned from the previous training. The first few minutes of training didn't slow him down at all, so I adjusted again. After three or four minutes of the new training, he suddenly stopped screaming and kicking. He smiled at his mom, pointed to the movie I was playing and started laughing. He calmed down completely and reverted to a cheerful, happy kid. It was kind of amazing. The mom couldn't believe it. She had never seen one of his tantrums "flip" like that.

After three more training session for reinforcement, his mother reported that his meltdowns had stopped. I suggested we stop training and wait until he melted down again before restarting. He never did. Since meltdowns were the only reason they were seeing us, there was no need to keep training him.

Two cases of quick anxiety relief

A 45-year-old man came into our office with extreme anxiety. He had been seeking relief for over a year through a variety of therapies, including medications. Nothing had worked. After his first neurofeedback session, he reported feeling significantly calmer. He said he had not experienced anything that could calm him like that.

A 27-year-old woman came to us suffering from extreme anxiety that had begun four months earlier following an assault. Medications hadn't helped. The anxiety had become so severe that she had to quit work. After her second neurofeedback session, she described herself as "feeling kind of normal," which hadn't happened since the event. She could not believe she could feel calm like that again.

Be aware that a single session does not solve a problem, but in 70 percent of our super-anxious cases, clients notice significant calming within a few sessions. It can take more time for the benefits to produce lasting effects. Once we see this kind of positive response to training, it's usually just a matter of time before it starts to hold. It often gives clients hope when they experience a big change, even for a short time, particularly when nothing else has worked. Most of these clients <u>have already been on multiple medications</u> before they came to us.

> Note: As soon as someone's anxiety kicks back in (the effects rarely hold for long during the first few sessions), they often believe that the neurofeedback didn't work. In fact, it *did* work. Their brain was able to calm itself. It just hadn't had enough practice yet to sustain its new "habit." I point out that they saw a glimpse of what they can achieve with practice.

The woman with the sluggish brain

A woman sought help for symptoms resulting from a brain aneurysm nine years earlier. She had trouble expressing herself, reading, writing well and remembering names. Her brain was very sluggish. It was almost painful to talk with her, because it took her so long to express herself. She had tried numerous therapies recommended by her doctors, but nothing helped. She had no hope and no options for improving until she heard about our program.

After two months of neurofeedback training, she was able to express herself better and faster and have real conversations. Her memory started to improve, as did her ability to read, write and make decisions. Her daughter described her mother as "more like herself." Her brain started to work again. She still had a long way to go but made remarkable gains in a short time.

Test-taking struggles

The mother of an intelligent 11th grader described her daughter's main problem as "being anxious and overwhelmed during tests." She studied and was prepared but did not perform well. If she was uncertain about a question, she couldn't get past it, interfering with her ability to complete the test. Based on her history and problem, I didn't think it would take long to have an impact.

Initially, we targeted training for anxiety. After four sessions, she reported doing a little better, but not as much as I expected. I suspected there was more going on. Often what sounds like anxiety or being overwhelmed by tests can be something else that shows up in high-demand situations.

After switching to a different neurofeedback protocol that targets processing and self-confidence, we did two more sessions. After those two sessions, she reported dramatically better results and completed several tests with no problem. After two more sessions, she said she felt clearer, more certain and confident. She had begun interacting better in the classroom and performed faster while taking tests. Because she was doing well, she stopped training. We can't be sure if the training was enough to hold forever, but it clearly had a big impact. At times, a little shift will go a long way.

Too anxious to drive

A 40-year-old mother of three had anxiety caused by major trauma. It was so extreme that she was unable to drive. Even riding in the car as a passenger distressed her. She would stare at the floor the entire time the car was moving, just to endure the ride.

After 10 minutes of her first neurofeedback session, she reported feeling a little more anxious. I adjusted the training, and ten minutes later she said she felt calmer than when she came in. After eight sessions, she reported being able to drive short distances and feeling far less anxiety. She wasn't "cured" after eight sessions, due to the extreme level of trauma and the number of years she had been experiencing anxiety. However, five additional sessions brought her significant improvement and kept her from reverting to the anxiety level she had experienced for years. She benefited from a combination of both neurofeedback and another type of biofeedback. Given her history, I expected her to need more sessions than she did in order to achieve this level of benefit.

14-year-old girl missing school due to anxiety

An academically gifted 14-year-old freshman experienced so much anxiety at school that she sometimes refused to go. She frequently wound up in the nurse's office complaining of severe anxiety or stomach distress. She was even fearful of using the school bathroom. She called her mother (a mental health therapist) at work five to 10 times a day, pleading for her to come get her. This was extremely stressful for her mom.

After eight training sessions, the number of times she called her mom had dropped to only a few calls a week. She stopped refusing to go to school and became comfortable using the school restroom. As training progressed, the girl reported noticeably less anxiety, as well as improved ability to manage herself. In 14 sessions, the girl felt much happier and had only moderate, controllable anxiety. Her mom was thrilled for her daughter and thankful that the frantic calls had stopped.

Two years later her anxiety began ramping up, but before it got out of control, she returned for a "tune-up." (It's not uncommon for someone to need an occasional tune-up.) After four sessions, she got back on track and didn't need to continue training.

Man with long-term depression gets off meds

We worked with a 32-year-old man who had lived with depression since he was a pre-teen. He'd been on numerous medications and tried many lifestyle changes like yoga, meditation and diet. None of these helped much.

The stress of a high-pressure job with a big company exacerbated his symptoms. Functioning at work had become more and more difficult. He was easily agitated. He had trouble expressing himself, and he found himself withdrawing from the people at work with whom he needed to interact. He also had negative thoughts that worried him.

This client felt his antidepressant was preventing his depression from getting worse, but it didn't stop all his symptoms and likely never would. There were also side effects. He didn't want to live the rest of his life taking medication.

He committed to doing neurofeedback to see if it could help him get a handle on his problem. As a technical troubleshooter for a large company, he understood it would take time to get his brain even and stable. He was prepared to stick with the training, because he wanted to get off meds and had learned enough to believe that neurofeedback could help. He knew it might not be an easy road, but his long journey with medications had been particularly challenging.

I did a brain map on him to more accurately target his training. It identified a distinct pattern commonly associated with depression and anxiety. Because he had dealt with this problem for 20 years, I didn't expect it to resolve quickly.

By the third session, his mood was already improving. By his seventh visit, he reported his mood was often a 7 out of 10 after a session, much better than before, but the improvement didn't hold more than a day or two. There were times he reported not doing well after a session. It took a number of sessions before the benefits started to hold longer.

All of these factors meant I had to do numerous adjustments to his training. It helped that he was very in-tune with himself and able to make astute observations about his responses.

To help cement his training, I recommended he take some vitamin supplements (see Appendix) that I've found helpful for people suffering from mood, depression and anxiety issues. I suggested he stop drinking diet soda, which may have been negatively impacting his mood. After a few weeks, he identified that both of those steps helped him progress and be more stable.

After 25 sessions, he asked his doctor to work with him to lower his meds. At that point I added other biofeedback to his neurofeedback training to help smooth the transition.

After 35 sessions, because of improvement in his mood, more stability in his mood and greatly reduced meds, he discontinued regular training. He continues to do maintenance sessions once every two to four months to keep him on track.

Woman gets off meds for depression after 15 years

A 54-year-old woman with depression and anxiety came to me after being on antidepressants for 15 years, 10 of them on

Wellbutrin. She had tried unsuccessfully several times to get off her medication because of side effects.

A qEEG revealed a pattern common to depression over the left frontal/temporal area, along with an anxiety profile over the right temporal area. We designed a targeted neurofeedback protocol to help her train.

After 15 neurofeedback sessions, she began working with her doctor to reduce and then discontinue her medication, which occurred smoothly. She was off her medications after 23 sessions, without any of the challenges she had experienced previously trying to lower meds. She felt stable for the first time in years.

She had positive effects during the first three sessions, but the day after the fourth session, she called to report she had cried all morning. Crying isn't a common response, and we can't say that it was a response to neurofeedback training, but it's typically easy to correct. I asked her to come to my office later that day to train with a different protocol. She smoothed out after 15 minutes of training and said she felt much better. After that adjustment, she had no more emotional events and made steady progress going forward.

To help ensure she maintains her gains, we see her every two-to-four months for a couple of sessions.

In my opinion, anyone with long term-depression should have continuing support (exercise, neurofeedback maintenance, nutrition or other programs) in order to help sustain their gains. It's possible the gains from neurofeedback will hold without it. However, research shows that chronic depression has a high rate of recurrence, so it makes sense to be proactive.

Nurse practitioner migraine relief

A nurse practitioner suffered from migraine headaches for nearly 40 years. They were so severe that several times a year she ended up in the emergency room. It would take her at least a day to recover. Migraine medications usually helped her through the worst of the headache—but not always. They certainly didn't fix the problem.

Over her first 10 neurofeedback sessions, she noticed improvements. Those included fewer migraines and less intense, shorter-duration migraines. On those occasions when she arrived with a migraine, it was almost gone by the end of the session.

About 12 sessions into our training, she woke up one morning with a severe migraine. Her husband brought her to our office at 9 a.m., hoping to avoid taking her to the hospital. She had been throwing up for hours and described her pain as a "15 on a 10-point scale." After about 40 minutes of training, which required some customized adjustments, she reported that her pain had gone from a 15 to a 3. Her husband, a skeptical engineer, told me he was amazed. He'd been to the hospital many times with her and never seen her recover so quickly or well.

By the time she had completed 25 neurofeedback sessions, the client was experiencing consistently fewer and less intense migraines and was no longer taking migraine medications. After 10 additional sessions to solidify her gains and to work on some anxiety issues, she remained nearly migraine-free more than a year later. We see her for a session every month or two for a tune-up.

Over 20 years, I've observed that if an experienced neurofeed-back provider trains someone who is <u>actively having a migraine</u>, 75 percent of the time that person will experience a significant reduction in pain within 30 minutes.

Eight-year-old girl with migraine headaches

An eight-year-old girl had missed more than a third of the previous school year due to migraine headaches, which had been occurring for two years. She had been seen by several neurologists, who had been unable to help her. A week before a scheduled third MRI, her parents brought her to see me in the middle of a migraine. She ranked her pain as almost 8 of 10 when she arrived. After 20 minutes of training, she said her headache was barely noticeable. Because of the severity of the problem, we suggested that her mother bring her in the next day for training, and again two days afterward.

At that point, the headaches stopped. The parents canceled the third MRI and brought their daughter in for more neurofeedback—waiting to see what happened. We trained her about 25 times to be sure the training had stabilized her improvement. We tracked her for the next two years. During that time, although she had an occasional headache, the migraines did not return nor did they prevent her from attending school.

Mental health therapist's migraines stop after two months of neurofeedback training

A 31-year-old mental health therapist had been suffering from migraine headaches since the age of 12. She had learned to just "power through" them but wanted to try neurofeedback as a last resort.

She reported having one or two migraines per week, lasting one-to-four days. On the second day of a migraine, she called us for an emergency session. After 25 minutes of training, her migraine went from a 7 out of 10 to a 2. She exclaimed that there was "no way" that kind of headache could have gone away so quickly. The shortest relief from any other sort of remedy she had ever used was waking up without a headache the next morning.

After six more weekly sessions, she reported that her migraines had stopped. Shortly thereafter she decided to add neurofeedback to her practice.

Note regarding migraines. There's no way to predict in advance if someone's migraine will respond to neurofeedback. The cases above are similar to ones I hear regularly from colleagues around the world. Most experienced clinicians tell me that 75-85% of migraineurs gain significant benefit from neurofeedback. This statistic is in line with my own experience, plus there are two published studies that support similar numbers. We can't pinpoint the exact mechanism that explains why it works, but in the same vein, science also can't explain exactly how migraines are created.

I often tell clients, "If your brain is good at creating a headache, neurofeedback can help your brain learn how take your headache away." It's a simple way to explain it, and seems to be true for many clients.

Damp dirt trauma

A woman who had been a nurse in humid Vietnam during the war experienced a major traumatic event that occurred on damp ground. When she returned to the U.S, she settled in Clemson, South Carolina where it rained a lot. Periodically, the smell of damp earth would re-trigger her trauma. She had significant post-traumatic stress disorder (PTSD).

After leaving the service, she became a mental health therapist with the goal of helping herself and others. For 25 years she traveled the U.S., trying every type of trauma therapy and treatment she could find, to no avail. Then she discovered neurofeedback.

She reported that during her tenth session of alpha-theta (a special type of neurofeedback training often used for trauma), she found herself in a profoundly deep state. In that state she visualized the events that had created her trauma in Vietnam. This time, however, she felt herself floating above those events and watching from afar as an observer. Instead of being fearful and in pain, she was able to distance herself from it.

After that session, she said the trauma never affected her again in the same way, even when the smell of damp dirt wafted through her window. She knew it happened. The memory would never go away, but it no longer triggered her. Her neurofeedback training allowed her to start living normally again.

Cry me a river...

A 51-year-old client with a 16-year-old daughter was referred to me by her therapist. She had lost her husband a year before. Every day she cried. She'd go around the corner in her house, see a reminder and cry. Her daughter would ask her a question, and she would cry. Any memory of her late husband caused her to cry. After this had gone on for a year, her therapist decided to send her to me to see if neurofeedback could help.

My role was to place sensors on her head and select the neurofeedback program most appropriate for her situation. There was no therapy, no discussion of crying. The training exercise targeted the part of the brain I call the "emotional resilience circuit" over the left temporal lobe.

When the client returned for her eighth session, she reported that her crying had stopped and was no longer an issue. We did two more sessions to support her change, but no more were needed. It was like a switch had flipped. The crying simply stopped.

We never discussed her husband or grief. Had she had other issues, like long-term depression, it probably would have taken longer.

> I've had this type of experience multiple times with "criers." The temporal lobe plays a critical role in emotional regulation, so training that part of the brain often produces a notable effect.

No motivation millennial

A 21-year-old woman living at home with her mother for the last three years lacked all motivation to work or attend school. Her room was a disaster. She had been a top student in high school until the age of 18 when there was some sort of drug incident that had thrown her off-track (her mother didn't know what drug it was). She had never recovered.

During our initial consultation I noticed that she could not give a complete answer to any of my questions. She would start to answer, then go off on a tangent. I had to end the interview early because it was driving me crazy! I suggested we train her right then and there, using the information I already had.

I trained her left pre-frontal lobe because I suspected, based on my clinical experience, that that area had trouble sequencing information. The left pre-frontal lobe plays a vital role in that function. My suspicion was that hers was not working well. I thought that after training her, I'd get a better idea based on her response.

Short-term outcome: We trained on a Monday. When she came back on Wednesday, I was able to finish my interview. I got more complete, logical answers to my questions in a reasonable amount of time. Her mother reported being shocked that the day after her first training session she cleaned up part of her room, something she hadn't done in a long time. Following the next few trainings, she went out and socialized with a friend, which she had not been doing.

This progress didn't mean her problem was fixed. However, experiencing that amount of noticeable change in 30 minutes of training was kind of impressive to me. It took 25 more sessions for her to demonstrate consistent improvement, but her quick response indicated that her brain was still intact, for the most part, despite whatever damage or disruption the drug event might have had.

Long-term outcome: Four months later she decided to go back to school.

Like many clients, this young woman experienced a delayed response to training. In a relatively short time, she cleaned up her room for the first time and started socializing. However, the major changes took several months to "kick in."

Not all the effects are going to be instant. *It can take time for changes to translate into longer-term results.* I've seen many clients do better—months after completing training—with improvements well beyond what they noted at the time they quit.

The angry psychiatrist

Students in my intermediate Neurofeedback 201 course included a psychiatrist and 10 other professionals. The psychiatrist reported a tendency toward anxiety, mood issues and difficulty getting going in the morning. As part of a class demo, I did some activation training with her over the left sensory-motor strip, a few inches above the left ear. That protocol is known to help people wake more easily and be more alert.

Two minutes into the training she said, "I'm feeling more awake." You could see her sit up straighter. After another minute, she reported feeling even more alert. She said she felt really good and started smiling. It was clear her mood had lifted. She looked brighter and more upbeat. She seemed happier and less withdrawn.

She had reported anxiety as part of her history. I asked if she wanted to train for that also. She agreed. I switched to train on the right side, which is typically helpful for anxiety and calming.

Sometimes, you should leave success alone.

About a minute and a half into training, the psychiatrist said, "I don't know if I like this." Then she blurted out, "I don't like this!" Next, she yelled, "I don't like you!" I immediately stopped the training. Irritated and annoyed, she demanded, "Why did you do that to me?"

I quickly switched back to the left side and continued training. After about a minute, you could see her face shift from angry to more relaxed. She sighed. Within another minute, she was smiling again and said she was feeling good. Her irritation and anger had gone away completely.

What can we learn from what happened that day? (1) Even the most experienced clinician may need to make protocol adjustments. There's no way to predict how everyone will respond; (2) Some people, like this psychiatrist, are hyper-responsive to neurofeedback; and (3) It's amazing how quickly someone can feel better when you identify the correct training for them.

The tiny percentage of people who are hyper-responders to two or three minutes of neurofeedback tend to be hyper-responders to a lot of other things that can overwhelm their nervous system. They're sometimes called "sensitives" or "super-sensitives." I like to say these are people who can get thrown off if the wind blows the wrong way. That kind of nervous system is tricky to medicate. The people around them often don't understand their hyper-sensitivities or how to deal with them.

Neurofeedback is particularly good for hyper-sensitives because it can be exquisitely fine-tuned for each individual. For example, in the psychiatrist's case, training her brain to be more resilient and less easily shifted would help her immensely, but her provider has to know how to deal with someone wired that way.

40-year-old mental health clinician who couldn't quiet his racing mind

A mental health therapist came to my Neurofeedback 101 course. Each participant receives five neurofeedback sessions. When we discussed his training goals, he told me that his mind had been racing since he was young and that he endured non-stop conversations in his head.

For his first three sessions, we trained his temporal lobe (emotional calming), combined with his anterior cingulate (associated with a racing mind). Based on his feedback, we made some training adjustments for his fourth session. Toward the end of that 15-minute session, he reported a complete quieting of his mind. We did the same training one more time before he left the course. He reported later that the effect had lasted for several days. He could not remember experiencing that kind of calm mind in his life. These initial sessions showed him what he could accomplish if he trained more. He decided after his brief experience to include neurofeedback in his practice and to continue to train himself as well.

VA vet nightmares

A veteran had been awakened around 2 a.m. every morning since 1979 with nightmares, after three or four hours of sleep. He would get up, sit on his porch and smoke cigarettes, waiting for the sun to rise. Nothing the VA offered had helped, including psychotherapy and a variety of psychiatric medications.

The process of helping him with sleep and nightmares had ups and downs. He was very complicated and traumatized. His brain was stuck and not easy to shift. He was on five psych meds, which often slows training. After four months of training, which included both neurofeedback and biofeedback, his nightmares were reduced to one or two a week. He also began sleeping five to six hours a night, sometimes even seven, though these improvements didn't stick.

After about seven months, the sleep benefits began lasting two to four days. That was remarkable given his history and the fact that nothing had ever helped his sleep before. However, I knew that the benefits wouldn't hold longer without additional training and lowering his meds. After symptoms start to improve, some people find having their doctor start to lower their meds can be helpful. (See further discussion in Part 3 Frequently Asked Questions about Neurofeedback.)

He'd been on psychiatric medications for 40 years and had no interest in changing or lowering them. He didn't want to discuss it or allow me to talk with his psychiatrist about it.

This was not one of my success stories. This client quit before he had had enough training for his gains to hold, and his five psychiatric medications seemed to complicate training progress. However, I believe that if he had stayed with it, and agreed to lower his meds (which were interfering with the training), he might have realized significant, long-term benefit.

Desperate for sleep

We treated a 55-year-old man who had chronic sleep problems. He got less than 20 minutes of deep sleep a night, which is considered abnormally low. He'd seen numerous sleep doctors and primary care doctors. None of their suggestions had worked. He was desperate and felt his sleep was causing significant impairment. There was nothing more they could recommend.

Over the course of about 15 training sessions (primarily LENS training, which stands for low energy neurofeedback system), his sleep consistently improved. After another 10 sessions, he reported that his sleep had completely normalized. Over the course of the next 12 months, he came in about five times for tune-ups, which helped him keep his sleep on track. He told me, "Neurofeedback saved my life." He now comes once or twice a year for tune-ups.

Profoundly delayed 11-year-old boy

An 11-year-old boy I trained appeared to be severely mentally challenged. If his mother asked him to pick up an item for her in a store and she'd point to it, he couldn't do it. When I asked him what he liked to do or watch, he was unable to respond intelligibly. He couldn't carry on any kind of conversation. Talking to him was a lot like talking to a three- or four-year-old. In addition to delayed speech and slow processing, he struggled to make decisions or follow even one-step instructions (poor executive function).

After three sessions of targeting his language and attentional systems, his brain seemed to turn on. He began understanding more, became far more aware and could respond more appropriately to questions. His mother said he was now able to make some independent decisions and find requested items in a store for her. His school performance improved dramatically. He still had a long way to go but was doing better.

That level of progress in so few sessions in a case like this is rare. We used a newer type of neurofeedback that I feel often works faster for processing issues. Even with the new neurofeedback, he nevertheless exceeded any expectations I had for his progress. I would never have thought he could be this good. He required many more sessions to build on his improvements, but his improvements were impressive—he's a different kid than the one who walked in our door. It reminds me that it's impossible to predict how much improvement can occur with neurofeedback until you try.

The man whose wife thought he had Asperger's (he didn't)

A 48-year-old man was sent to see me by his wife, a special ed teacher. She was convinced he had undiagnosed Asperger's syndrome, characterized by extremely poor social communications. When we first met, he looked fearful and nervous as he stared at the floor. He told me that even after five years of working at the same company as an engineer, he *felt nervous every time he had to interact with co-workers*. I suspected that he had severe social anxiety and trained for that.

On the day of his 15th session, he saw me at a distance walking down the hall. He yelled hello and waved at me. As we got closer, he came over and said, "Hey, Mike, how's it going?" He reached out and shook my hand confidently before following my technician to his session. I could have fallen over. He was like a different person. After a few more sessions, he found a better job and moved out of the area with his family. I don't think that transition could have happened easily without having trained his brain.

OCD post-concussion carpenter who kept restarting his work

A 51-year-old carpenter had suffered from severe OCD (obsessive-compulsive disorder) since the age of 20. The OCD came a year after a car accident that had produced a significant concussion. He reported that he had had no symptoms of OCD before the accident.

The first time we met I asked him to describe his OCD. He said that within seconds, he noticed everything in my office that was out of order. There was a slightly discolored ceiling tile. The folders and pens on my desk weren't straight. He detected a small string lying on the floor (plus about five other things before I stopped him). All of those really bothered him.

At work, when doing a job, if something wasn't perfect, he would have to start over. Sometimes he could not complete a job after scrapping his work too many times. His OCD interfered seriously with his livelihood.

Because of his history of concussions, I started by doing a qEEG brain map on him. It indicated significant problems in his prefrontal lobe (decision-making, hyper-focus) and the anterior cingulate (stuck, obsessive thoughts, inflexibility, inability to transition) and some other areas. Some of his brainwaves ran too fast and others too slowly—at the same time. He was able to hyper-focus on details but couldn't slow down to see the big picture.

After about 20 sessions, he reported he had recently hung some pictures in his house and saw the task "as other people did" for the first time. Instead of taking an excessively detailed approach to every aspect of hanging the pictures, which in the past would have taken him several hours, he instead was able to step back and be "OK" with getting them up in a reasonable way. He said it took less than an hour to hang them. This was remarkable for him. He also noticed being far more relaxed and not "consumed" as much by details. Continued training was probably needed to help reinforce his gains but, unfortunately, he was injured in an accident and never made it back to training.

Note on OCD: Many people we see with OCD have done *everything*—including meds—with very limited effect. Neurofeedback helps turn people's lives around and allows them to function better and with more flexibility. It's a powerful tool for OCD. I've heard similar reports from many colleagues, even though the research is limited. For severe OCD, my experience is that it can take numerous neurofeedback sessions, plus ongoing maintenance. Other factors can also play a role in speeding up the training, including exercise, diet and nutrition. It's unfortunate that most people with OCD, and health professionals, are unaware of how helpful neurofeedback is.

There are some vitamins I recommend that seem to help many of our OCD clients make faster training progress with neurofeedback. See the Appendix for information.

Woman with 30 hot flashes a day

This client couldn't get through one day of work or one night of sleep without being tormented by severe hot flashes—more than 30 a day.

Jackets and towels were her constant companions at work. One moment she would be freezing and needed to put on her jacket. The next moment she had to peel off everything to try to cool down, frantically wiping off sweat and hoping no one would notice.

She never got more than a couple of hours of uninterrupted sleep on any given night. The covers went on. The covers went off. She would awake burning up, her clothing and bedding soaked. She'd grab a bath towel, dry off, change the sheets and her nightclothes, then try to sleep some more before this terrible cycle repeated itself. And, of course, the fan went on, and the fan went off.

After just three sessions of neurofeedback within the span of 17 days, training a type of neurofeedback called infraslow, most of her hot flashes were gone. She did two more sessions of neurofeedback. She reported that the hot flashes were down to a few a week and were much less intense.

> Note: We've had other women who reported significant hot flash improvement from training. There's no research in this realm as to why hot flashes can improve so dramatically. It appears that the brain is resetting some mechanism of hormonal regulation. Other clinicians have reported similar effects with hot flashes with various types of training. In the cases I've seen recently, most women experienced at least small changes within three to five sessions. How many sessions it takes to sustain benefits varies significantly.

A nurse with panic attacks

A 27-year-old client finally had her dream job as an R.N. in a hospital. The problem was, she was nearly crippled by anxiety and frequent panic attacks.

"For over a year, each day that I went to work I had a panic attack," she explained. "I thought, 'Oh, my God, I can't do this!' It was so much responsibility. I had people's lives in my hands."

Daily Xanax and an antidepressant helped a bit, but she still struggled badly, even on medications. And she didn't want to keep taking them. She feared her career could be in jeopardy.

"I reached the point where I had to do something," she recalled. "I couldn't go on like this. I was so anxious I couldn't think straight. I knew I wouldn't be able to continue to work in my profession if I didn't get a handle on this problem."

When a friend told her that neurofeedback might help, she decided to try it, even though she didn't know much about it. Since I've worked extensively with anxiety and panic attacks, we went straight into training without a brain map. My approach included neurofeedback and biofeedback that targeted systems playing a role in her chronic anxiety and panic attacks.

She came once a week. After her first session, she noticed that she was notably calmer. Following her sixth session, she felt calm enough to discontinue her medications. After her tenth session, she decided she was done and discontinued her training. This was a case where a combination of neurofeedback and biofeedback worked quickly.

"I was doing so well I didn't think I needed any more training," she said. "I was thinking much more clearly and had more confidence taking care of my patients. My panic attacks were gone."

It could have taken much longer than 10 sessions to stabilize her level of anxiety and panic attacks, but she was young, physically healthy and ate well. It's an example of how you can't predict how long neurofeedback and biofeedback might take to produce results. We followed her for several months after her training. Without additional sessions, she reported her symptoms were still under control.

20-year-old ADHD male pulled out of college, then returns and succeeds

A 20-year-old client had always struggled academically. It took a lot of work to make B's and C's in high school.

At college, he earned a mere 1.5 GPA in his first semester at a prestigious college in the Southeast. He improved little in his second semester. He was working hard but didn't test well. He struggled to be organized, stay on task, and complete assignments on time. He also had problems sleeping. He was placed on probation and sent back home to "get his act together."

His parents brought him to our center for neurofeedback training. A brain map showed that his brain was inefficient in areas related to attention but also in areas related to processing, comprehension and organization. We used this information to customize his training protocols to target those problems, along with improving his sleep.

We used single-channel training and a type of two-channel coherence neurofeedback training protocol, based on the map, to target his key "weak" areas. These included the frontal lobe, parietal lobe, temporal lobe, anterior cingulate and the occipital lobe.

His sleep normalized fairly quickly. We continued to train once a week over about five months. A follow-up brain map showed significant changes in his brain activity compared to the first map, although there were still a few areas that needed targeting. We continued to train based on the new targets. It was clear the training had helped him in the job he was doing part-time.

When he returned to school, his GPA zoomed up to 3.5. His test scores and productivity greatly improved, and he was better able to ignore distractions. One of his advisors remarked that to see that sort of turnaround after just one semester (and one summer) off was "quite amazing."

"Doing neurofeedback was a turning point for me," he said. "I was trying to figure it out on my own and wasn't succeeding. Working with the Center enabled me to push back the blocks."

The fact is, the neurofeedback helped him "work out" key circuits in his brain consistently over a five-month period, resulting in better school performance.

After four-plus years of silence, autistic boy starts speaking

We worked with a seven-year-old boy who was diagnosed with low-functioning autism. He had stopped speaking as a young child and hadn't spoken in nearly five years. He was also prone to occasional out-of-control attacks on his father and younger sister.

Over multiple months of training at our center, we targeted areas to calm him and reduce his outbursts. Later we trained the left frontal/temporal areas that play a critical role in speech.

After just a few sessions, his behavior was noticeably improved, though it took numerous sessions for him to gain and maintain more appropriate control. One day, after eight months of once- or twice-weekly neurofeedback sessions, he spoke in a complete sentence. He told his father, who was encouraging him to finish his homework: "I don't want to!" His father was thrilled.

The combination of neurofeedback, along with other therapies, started to take hold, and he continued to talk and add words. The dad credits neurofeedback with getting his son restarted speaking and calming down at school and at home.

Cognitive sharpening

A 74-year-old retired psychologist came to us to work on being calmer. In the process of working with her, it became clear that she was not as cognitively sharp as she should have been at her age. She had difficulty keeping up with detailed conversations and basic instructions. I trained her over the winter, targeting processing speed and anxiety. The following summer, she trained with someone in her hometown up north When she returned nine months later, she was noticeably sharper and better able to keep up with details and follow instructions. She reported that not only did she feel as sharp as she had in her late 40's but her anxiety was much more under control.

Other Cases for the Future

I thought about including cases from other providers, but I had so many good ones, I was concerned that it would make this book too long.

I hope in the near future to create a website link to encourage cases to be posted for educational purposes by other professionals. A lot of what I've learned in the field came from case examples shared freely by other providers.

Here are some categories that need more case examples:

- Sensory processing disorder
- Epilepsy/seizure disorder
- Bipolar disorder
- Attachment disorder/RAD
- Autism
- Stroke

- Brain fog from cancer, Lyme disease, traumatic brain injury (TBI), etc.
- Post-traumatic stress disorder (PTSD)
- Substance abuse cases
- TBI and concussions
- Parkinson's disease
- Alzheimer's disease and dementia
- Dyslexia (major reading issues)
- Dyscalculia (major problems with math)
- Tics and Tourette's syndrome
- Auditory processing issues
- Fine and gross motor function
- Executive function disorder
- Misophonia (abnormally strong, negative reaction to normal human sounds like chewing/breathing)
- Peak performance in sports and business

Read more neurofeedback client stories on our website: https://www.centerforbrain.com/client-stories/.

PART 3

Frequently Asked Questions about Neurofeedback

We've explained some basics of neurofeedback, but you probably have LOTS of other questions. Scan through the list below to see what might be helpful to you.

Some of the questions review material included earlier in the book. Most do not.

I created this chapter as an easy reference.

Included are many questions I haven't seen carefully answered in writing before.

1. Is there solid research on neurofeedback?
2. What does neurofeedback do?
3. How is neurofeedback different from Lumosity, brain games or mindfulness?
4. What problems does neurofeedback help?
5. What's the age range of people who can be trained?
6. What do I have to do during a neurofeedback session?
7. Does neurofeedback work even if I don't pay attention?
8. How can hearing a beep or watching a game or video help my brain change?

9. Are you putting anything in my brain when I train?
10. Can I use neurofeedback while on medication?
11. Can neurofeedback help me get off medication?
12. Can training impact the response to psychiatric or neurological medications?
13. Can I train with neurofeedback if I'm using marijuana, alcohol or other drugs?
14. How quickly can I expect to notice effects—and do they stick?
15. How many sessions will it take before I reach my goals?
16. Can you keep your brain in great shape without maintenance?
17. What if progress is inconsistent or slow?
18. Could neurofeedback make me worse?
19. When does neurofeedback not work?
20. Are there environmental factors that can impact training success?
21. Can medical or metabolic factors impact training success?
22. If neurofeedback is so darn good, why hasn't my doctor or therapist told me about it?
23. Why don't more health care providers offer neurofeedback?
24. How do I know the improvement was the result of neurofeedback, not other treatments that finally "kicked in?"
25. Do I have to want to participate in the training for neurofeedback to work?
26. Is all neurofeedback the same?
27. Can I do neurofeedback training at home?
28. What is a brain map (qEEG) and why have one?

29. Is a brain map necessary to do neurofeedback?

30. Where can I find the best neurofeedback practitioner?

1. Is there solid research on neurofeedback?

Yes…much of it spanning 40+ years. It includes newer fMRI brain scan research[11] (for example by Harvard-trained psychiatrist Ruth Lanius. M.D.[12]) which identifies changes in connectivity across the brain as a result of neurofeedback.

At a conference in 2019, Australian psychologist and neurofeedback practitioner Moshe Perl, Ph.D. presented an in-depth review of the published studies[13] in the field of neurofeedback and neuromodulation. The review found 314 studies that met their stringent criteria for inclusion as solid studies. Two hundred ninety-eight of those had positive outcomes, covering a variety of conditions. This review showed that there is a strong evidence base supporting neurofeedback.

Reviewing the research is well beyond the scope of this book. You can find research on the NIH PubMed site (search "neurofeedback") or look on www.ISNR.org under resources (or just Google the term "ISNR Comprehensive Research[14]"). ISNR is a professional membership organization for neurofeedback. I've also provided a condensed list of some of the most readable research[15] at www.CenterForBrain.com along with links. Click on Learn, then click Research Papers.

There's an ever-increasing amount of research demonstrating neurofeedback's effectiveness. However, neurofeedback

---

[11] https://www.sciencedirect.com/science/article/pii/S1053811912009561

[12] https://www.ncbi.nlm.nih.gov/pubmed/23022326

[13] https://apjnt.org/wp-content/uploads/2019/05/David-_Perl_APJNT_Journal_Vol1_No1_2019.pdf

[14] https://www.isnr.org/isnr-comprehensive-bibliography

[15] https://www.centerforbrain.com/neurofeedback/neurofeedback-research/

(or any field) can be criticized for not having enough research. It would be nice to have outcome studies for neurofeedback with every possible brain condition. Unfortunately, it's been impossible in this field to get that kind of funding and support.

2. What does neurofeedback do?

The neurofeedback computer program constantly measures specific brain activity. It alerts you instantly with FEEDBACK when your brain makes more or less of the activity being measured and monitored (the computer gives you feedback when you reproduce the desired pattern). Your brain responds by unconsciously reinforcing the feedback pattern.

This brain "exercise" appears to improve the efficiency of your brain patterns or in some way help the brain reorganize its function. The result is better attention, emotions, mood, processing and more. The key to sustained change is repetition (practice, practice, practice). That's why a series of neurofeedback sessions is usually necessary.

3. How is neurofeedback different from Lumosity, brain games or mindfulness?

Video games, brain games like Sudoku, software training like Lumosity and BrainHq and mindfulness training can be powerful. However, they do not directly measure specific brain activity and give instant (real-time) feedback like neurofeedback does. When exposed to neurofeedback, the brain responds to the instant information it receives and changes or adapts its behavior as a result.

Neurofeedback technology helps measure and provide feedback about "brain circuit activity" that correlates to learning, expressing what you think, doing math, controlling emotions, paying attention, quieting your mind and far more. Powerful learning or adapting typically occurs when your brain gets instant feedback about specific brain patterns.

4. What problems does neurofeedback help?

Neurofeedback is commonly used to help any type of brain-specific challenges. These include ADHD, anxiety, depression, autism, cognitive and processing issues, sensory integration issues and sleep problems. It also helps with neurological issues such as the impact of concussion, traumatic brain injury (TBI), chronic pain, seizures, and migraines.

Can neurofeedback also help with substance abuse treatment?

Yes. It's increasingly used in clinicians' offices and addiction rehab centers. Studies and clinical experience show that neurofeedback is helpful for improving outcomes and reducing relapse.

People struggling with substance abuse issues typically have underlying issues like depression, anxiety and sleep. Neurofeedback provides a non-medication approach to gaining self-control, calming, emotions, executive function, sleep and anxiety. Training gives those in treatment a much better shot at "getting their act together." Research shows that neurofeedback training helps substance abuse clients stay in treatment longer, which increases the chances they will succeed.

If I have a medical, genetic or neurological problem, can neurofeedback help?

Often, yes. Neurofeedback doesn't treat any specific diagnosis or condition. It helps the brain increase efficiency and reorganize function. Therefore, no matter what caused your problem—brain injury, Alzheimer's disease, Parkinson's disease or genetics—training can be helpful.

With degenerative, neurological and genetic issues, no one can predict whose benefits will hold over time and whose will require steady training to maintain benefits. Ultimately, you only know by trying. If it's determined that regular maintenance training is needed to improve quality of life, families tell me it can be worthwhile. For example, I've seen neurofeedback training help people speak and interact with others and be more cognitively clear until the very end of their life—when they couldn't do so before training. There are many factors that can influence how long benefits last.

The research is very limited on how neurofeedback impacts *Alzheimer's disease* or *Parkinson's disease*. However, many clinicians have worked with clients, family members and friends with these conditions and reported consistent improvements. Sometimes improvement can be dramatic. Other times it's incremental. In my opinion, it's helpful to try. Even small changes can mean a lot, such as the ability to communicate better. You never know what is possible until you try.

Neurofeedback doesn't typically reverse a chronic degenerative neurological condition. What's more commonly reported are small improvements in function, with a slower decline. It can be as simple as more "good days" and fewer "bad days." It may require ongoing neurofeedback or maintenance sessions. Neurofeedback works better, in my opinion, as part of a comprehensive treatment approach, including an anti-inflammatory diet and supplements.

5. What's the age range of people who can be trained?

You can train the brain at almost any age, from 3 to 100. If learning can occur — even a little — then the brain can adapt.

My youngest client so far was 18 months old; my oldest clients are in their 90s. I trained a 91-year-old woman who had limited ability to communicate due to a stroke. After five sessions, she was communicating so normally that her 93-year-old husband remarked, "I've got my wife back."

A colleague successfully trained his *three-month-old son* to sleep better.

6. What do I have to do during a neurofeedback session?

Generally, all you do is sit in a room and receive auditory and/or visual feedback, which you can either pay attention to or ignore. Most people's brains respond to that feedback whether you pay attention or not.

Some neurofeedback practitioners like to explain the goals (what to pay attention to) during a session. Others don't describe goals. Some will tell you to close your eyes while training and just listen for the sounds. Based on my experience and conversations with many colleagues, all these approaches work. Is one better? It's hard to say. The types of activities include:

Various games that are tied to brain feedback

 A Pac-Man that moves; a movie that fades in or out or becomes smaller or larger based on your brain activity; racing cars; making a rocket ship go.

- Various types of sounds which change as your brain pattern changes. Optionally, you may train with your eyes closed, just listening to the feedback sounds.
- You can watch your EEG patterns on a monitor and try to make the waves taller or shorter.

Some providers train clients while engaged in a cognitive task (reading, studying, even therapy).

7. Does neurofeedback work even if I don't pay attention?

Yes. Would music affect you if you weren't paying attention to it? If I told you I wanted you to listen to a song that you had never heard, what would you have to do?

Just listen. No real effort is required. Your brain responds to music without your having to do anything.

You can often learn a song by simply listening. Your brain can learn music and responds to music without any effort. It's well-known that music can affect your mood.

Think of neurofeedback the same way. In most cases, you listen (or watch), and your brain figures out how to respond to the feedback (sound, visuals) with no effort on your part.

Some clinicians feel that learning may occur faster if someone has set goals and is engaging their attention. In my experience, active engagement is often not necessary for a neurofeedback training response. Many clients clearly respond to neurofeedback without any conscious awareness, just by getting feedback.

Note: Most clients aren't aware of the specific frequencies being trained or even if their brain is responding at all to feedback, yet they make progress.

8. How can hearing a beep or watching a game or video help my brain change?

The *type* of sound or visual feedback isn't the key. There's an infinite number of ways to provide visual, auditory and even tactile feedback.

You receive instant feedback from the neurofeedback whenever your brain makes a certain pattern, and your brain does the rest. It detects the pattern and quickly learns to make more of it. It might also use that pattern to adapt or disrupt existing patterns, allowing the brain to reorganize its function.

Because it's hard for people to grasp that the brain responds to feedback without attention or effort, here are two examples that illustrate the concept:

1. A mom at the playground is surrounded by other moms, all talking. Across the field, her five-year-old is playing with lots of noisy other kids. In the middle of a conversation, she jumps up and runs across the field because she heard trouble coming from her child. How did her brain know that her child's voice was escalating, considering all the other noise going on? It picked

out and responded to the particular pattern (the child's voice) that was significant to her brain.

2. You're at a loud party, paying close attention to a conversation. From across the room, you hear someone mention your name (meaning your brain responded to that "feedback"). With all the surrounding chatter, how did you notice? You weren't listening for your name, but you heard it.

Your brain is superb at identifying patterns that are important to it. It typically responds to the feedback from its own pattern by reinforcing or responding to the pattern being measured over time. The brain is an exquisite pattern-recognition machine.

9. Are you putting anything into my brain when I train?

No. Neurofeedback simply measures brain activity. The sensors placed on your head read activity coming from your brain, such as the EEG. That data is sent to the computer program which, in turn, provides auditory or visual feedback. It's the same concept as a blood pressure cuff that reads your pressure and relays it to the gauge on the cuff.

10. Can I use neurofeedback while on medication?

It's common for people to start training with neurofeedback while on psychiatric or neurological medications. If you're on a stable dose, you should be able to identify changes from the neurofeedback training independently from your meds with guidance from your neurofeedback provider. You should inform your neurofeedback provider in advance of any medications you're taking and how long you've been on them.

One class of drugs that may impede the effectiveness of neurofeedback is benzodiazepines (Xanax, Klonopin, Valium, Ativan). These medications interfere with short-term memory and learning. Any interference with learning can contribute to a slower response to neurofeedback training.

Even if you're on benzodiazepines, you may still do neurofeedback training. Talk to your provider to discuss the implications. Make sure that your provider is comfortable and familiar with the medications you are on, as well as the implications of neurofeedback in combination with those medications.

It doesn't generally make sense to start new psych meds at the same time as starting neurofeedback. It's too difficult to discern which therapy is causing which result. Starting a medication after you've been doing neurofeedback for a while is not as difficult. You can also start neurofeedback once you're clear about your response to a new medication. Discuss these issues with both your neurofeedback provider and your physician. They could have quite different views, particularly because many physicians have limited, if any, experience with neurofeedback and its potential impact on meds.

11. Can neurofeedback help me get off medication?

Many people who come for neurofeedback have the goal of lowering their meds or not relying on medications to manage symptoms. As improvements, or more stability of symptoms, occur from neurofeedback training, some children and adults are able to reduce or even eliminate their medications—even when previous efforts to lower the dose has failed.

Neurofeedback often appears to support and
stabilize the brain during the process of lowering meds.

Reducing or stopping a medication, however, requires careful coordination and communication between the patient and physician. A physician typically won't reduce medication simply because their patient is doing neurofeedback. They usually will reduce medication only if they observe that the patient is improving and/or expresses a desire for a medication change and/or is concerned about side effects.

The "improvement" dilemma

Unfortunately, it's common for a neurofeedback client who feels they are doing better, and wants to reduce their medication, to be told by their doctor, "You're doing well, let's not change the medications." In other words, if things are going well, why rock the boat? It's a logical question. The client may have to be proactive to engage in further discussion about their desires.

If the individual has been on medication for a while with no appreciable change, and improvements have occurred since doing neurofeedback, it's likely the improvements are coming from the neurofeedback. It's worth considering that lowering medications *while you are doing better* is the likely time to reduce. This is a discussion that needs to take place between the doctor and the patient. The patient needs to express clearly their desire for change.

The most cautious and successful approach I've observed is when the physician initially lowers one medication by a *small amount* and doesn't change the dose of any other meds. If the first dose is lowered with no ill effects, the physician usually feels more confident in gradually reducing medications further., step by step.

> Note: Sometimes coming off or lowering meds creates a "bump" or a rough patch that appears within one day to two weeks. If the person can hang in there as they get used to the lower dose, often, though not always, things smooth out. I have found that an extra session or two of neurofeedback over the first few days to two weeks after lowering the meds can smooth the bumps and help the client adapt more easily.

12. Can training impact the response to psychiatric or neurological medications?

Neurofeedback is compatible with medications, but the impact of medications on someone training with neurofeedback should be carefully observed and monitored.

Clinicians note that after a number of neurofeedback sessions, medications may have a slightly different effect than previously. Some argue that because training has improved the brain's activation and connectivity, you're no longer medicating the same brain you started with.

After neurofeedback training, medication may work better for some patients. In other cases, the medication may need to be adjusted. The medication may become too sedating, too activating or have other effects. I recommend you discuss this possibility with both your neurofeedback practitioner and your prescribing physician.

> **EXAMPLE**: A man on anti-anxiety medications started neurofeedback training. Initially, his anxiety was reduced and his sleep was good. After completing more sessions, he reported

feeling uncharacteristically sluggish. It was possible his symptoms were related to the impact of doing training while on meds. In other words, his medication possibly became more efficient (more sedating) because of training. This type of situation required a discussion with his physician.

I've had clients taking antidepressants who became more anxious when we tried to train the area of their brain most involved with depression. When their doctor lowered the dosage, the anxiety went away. That doesn't mean they didn't need the antidepressant previously. It simply indicated that as their brain changed, due to the neurofeedback training, the need for that previous amount of medication changed.

Keep in mind that there are factors other than neurofeedback that could be causing a different response to the meds including diet, lifestyle and environmental stressors.

13. Can I train with neurofeedback if I'm using marijuana, alcohol or other drugs?

It's possible to train with neurofeedback while using substances, but they may interfere with or slow neurofeedback progress. Success depends on many factors, including the type of substance, dosage, frequency, your age and overall clinical history. It's important to be frank about this with your neurofeedback provider so that you can have the best training experience possible and to be sure that the training you're doing is appropriate.

14. How quickly can I expect to notice effects—and do they stick?

About 70 percent of the kids and adults I work with notice some type of change within one to three sessions. Others take longer. Initially, the changes might be minor or temporary, like moments of feeling calmer or more alert, sleeping better, having more dreams or not reacting to a usual trigger (anything out of your ordinary patterns.).

Note: Some people are very unaware of themselves. They may not notice when they experience change, particularly subtle change. Many of my clients insist they've seen no change from training, At the same time, we get reports from those around them of subtle—and often not-so-subtle—changes.

It's easy to attribute change to other factors, but it might well be the impact of your training. Any behavior or feeling that's different than your "norm" should be reported to your provider.

A good way to assess changes is to ask yourself questions like, Did I do better on a task at work or at school? Did I feel less anxious in an environment that usually triggers me? Another good way is to enlist someone close to you to help you observe yourself.

Some people notice effects during or immediately after the training session. Others notice effects hours later or over the following day or two after training. The response to training may even bring symptoms to the surface that were already there but masked. (See the following question for more about this). In my opinion, any response you notice is an indication that your brain is responding to the new exercise.

Short-lived effects: Training effects that clients notice following the first few sessions may be *temporary*. These effects might last 10 minutes or two days, then evaporate. That's because training effects build over time. When benefits fade, more practice is needed until it sticks. Doing neurofeedback successfully is not unlike learning a language. It typically takes multiple exposures and practice sessions for new vocabulary words to stick in your brain. You easily forget them at the beginning until you've practiced enough.

It takes time for the benefits of training to accumulate. Since neurofeedback is a form of learning, some people learn faster than others. However, if you notice changes from the training, it's often just a matter of time before the new patterns stick. Part of the neurofeedback process is staying with it until you learn.

A BIG FRUSTRATION for clients, they tell me, is getting a positive effect from training and then LOSING it. They sleep well for a night. They feel less anxious or depressed for a short time....and then the benefit vanishes. That cycle may happen multiple times before benefits start to hold. I've seen people at this point want to quit, yet momentary improvements are evidence that the neurofeedback did *something* to help their brain learn to function better.

Any changes you notice are your brain's response to neurofeedback. That means **your brain can do this.** It's just not very good at the new pattern yet. It can take a *lot* of practice before you get so good at being calm or feeling happier or sleeping better that you don't have to practice. Until you learn it well (practice, practice, practice), you may notice "ups and downs."

Receiving positive encouragement during these ups and downs can be very important, particularly from friends, family and the provider.

Interesting fact: Neurofeedback often impacts sleep, anxiety and emotional control more quickly than other kinds of changes. Noticeable improvement in executive function issues like ADHD, attention, decision-making, staying on task and organizing generally takes longer and is more subtle.

15. How many sessions will it take before I reach my goals?

There's no "typical" number of sessions for any one client. Every person is unique and responds at a different pace. Experiencing a short-term response is common, but I don't consider training to be successful until the new pattern has stuck over time.

You don't have to wait months and months to see if neurofeedback is going to work, however. Most people will start to notice some change in 5-10 sessions. It's not uncommon to see small changes within two or three sessions. More training is almost always required to reinforce and enhance the changes.

Once improvement has been consistent over time, I suggest clients spread out how often they train (once a week, once every two weeks, etc.) and track to see if the benefits continue to hold. Many people use that as a basis for choosing when to slow down or stop training. Some experienced providers I know suggest slowing the training over a 6-12-month period, particularly for long-term chronic problems.

We've seen people resolve their target issues in 7-15 sessions, particularly those with "lighter" or more short-term problems. It's more common to need 25-40 sessions for benefits to hold well.

Many factors can influence how many sessions you need:

- the type of problem and its severity
- the length of time you've been dealing with the situation
- the presence of developmental issues
- a history of falls, car accidents or hits on the head
- diet and nutrition
- thyroid and hormone conditions
- gut/brain issues
- medications
- exposure to mold or chemicals

Some people, particularly with complicated or chronic conditions, may need more than 40 sessions to help *sustain* their improvements. This may seem like a lot, but what other approach will help you "re-wire" your brain and fundamentally change your life? How many lessons does it take to play the piano well? Or to learn to dance? Learning is different for everyone. Here are a couple of examples:

Among autistic children, you often see steady advances in attention, speech and expression, managing emotions, socializing, learning and behavior. Many parents have told me that the progress they saw with their child after adding neurofeedback exceeded progress they observed with any other intervention. I've also heard that neurofeedback training reduced the costs of special services (including shadows) for school and beyond.

Some of my autistic clients have had more than 60 training sessions but experienced noticeable benefits long before that. The parents continued bringing their children because they saw steady, incremental benefits.

Here's an example of a *complex concussion case* that required a lot of sessions. The client was a psychologist in her mid-60's.

She had experienced five concussions prior to seeing us. Her last concussion occurred more than a year before she came in for the first time. These concussions had thrown her off badly. She had difficulty working, was extremely forgetful, became easily confused, had a hard time driving and experienced mood issues. She struggled at times to think clearly.

Over the course of the first 10-20 sessions, she noticed significant improvements. However, the gains didn't fully hold, which is not uncommon with this condition. She had a lot of ups and downs, particularly early in training. She stuck with it and improved slowly but steadily. After 120 sessions she felt her brain was fully functional. In fact, she said she felt she was better than she had been since her late 40's. (My bet— most people would have quit much earlier.) We did several qEEG brain maps to keep the training on track.)

Frankly, this client exceeded any expectations I had for her. I would never have guessed she would have a complete recovery from multiple serious concussions at her age. It's kind of remarkable what the brain can do, given the chance. She did the work; I just guided the training. I give her great credit for being tenacious and refusing to give up. It paid off.

Three years after her last training, she reported that she had maintained her benefits without any maintenance training. All of her symptoms from post-concussion syndrome appeared resolved. Not only was her brain performing really well but she said she now planned to work into her late 80's. Her increased work productivity paid many times over for what she invested in neurofeedback training.

There's a small percentage of children and adults who need ongoing neurofeedback training or maintenance in order to continue to function well. Nevertheless, continuing neurofeedback training can be a much better option than a lifetime of struggling and taking medications. These cases probably justify getting a home system to use under the supervision of a knowledgeable provider.

16. Can you keep your brain in great shape without maintenance?

If we lived in a perfect world, you'd do neurofeedback training, get your brain on track—and be done. For some people, that's what happens. For others, however, their brain *"slips" or gets knocked off track at some point.*

Over the years it's become clear that LOTS of things can throw you off—sleep, diet, environment, electronics, extreme stress, medications, etc. If you're lucky enough to withstand this throughout your life, that's great, but "slipping" is not a failure of neurofeedback training. It's called life.

When your brain gets off—even a little bit—I've never seen anything help faster than neurofeedback.

Lots of people work really hard—with exercise, diet, supplements, yoga, meditation, etc. for months or longer—to get themselves back on track. Yet with neurofeedback, you can often get back on track in one or two sessions—literally in a few days. That's particularly true if you've had training before. It's great to have a tool like this to rely on when you need it.

We have lots of clients who come once a year or several times a year for one to three sessions. It depends on their life and their brain. Others stay on track and never need more.

A small percentage of clients need consistent maintenance training to sustain benefits. They are generally adults with long-term chronic psychiatric or neurological issues or children with complex developmental problems from early childhood. For those situations, I discuss with clients whether home training with supervision might be a useful option.

Tune-ups for school...work...aging

Neurofeedback tune-ups can help people tackle short-term goals.

For example, we occasionally do short-term training with teenagers right before a big test. The goal is to help with test anxiety or concentration issues. These are smart, functional kids who normally wouldn't come, who are overwhelmed and suffering from anxiety, overthinking and sleep issues. In our center, short-term trainings or maintenance run two to four sessions, depending on the goal.

I see adults whose stress at work all of a sudden got very intense—from a big meeting or presentation to a new boss. I see parents whose child is having a crisis that puts them "over the edge." In many cases, three to six sessions (sometimes mixed with other tools) can make a world of difference.

I take these cases selectively, as I can't always figure out the right training quickly. If the only factor is the upcoming high-stress event, I'm often able to help them perform better in just a few sessions.

<u>Tune-ups are also helpful for people who are aging and are concerned about staying sharp.</u> Many of my older clients tell me that neurofeedback helps them stay sharper as they age.

Let me tell you a little story about myself. When I was 57, I noticed that I occasionally struggled to come up with words I used all the time. Names were getting harder to remember. When my wife and an employee confronted me and expressed concern about my memory problems, I decided to do something about it. I'd been working too much and doing very little neurofeedback on myself. It was time I became my own client.

I devised a set of neurofeedback protocols that I used once a week. After three months, my word retrieval problem had noticeably improved. I've since trained myself about once per month ever since. My memory is now better than it's been in the last 15 years. I now sometimes surprise myself when I remember certain names, for example, but I've noticed that if I go too long without training, I can slip.

17. What if progress is inconsistent or slow?

People become frustrated when they experience minimal progress after 5-10 sessions, or their progress backslides. It's easy for them to feel like this doesn't work for them. Learning can take a while, and some people need more practice than others to "get it" and never forget it. Their brain has that old pattern down exceptionally well, and it easily falls back to its familiar pattern.

If you're not making good progress, it's possible you need a different training protocol. If you've been doing neurofeedback consistently and are dissatisfied with your progress, don't just stop. Ask your provider about other ways to train.

18. Could neurofeedback make me worse?

In my 20-plus years of doing neurofeedback, I personally haven't seen anyone doing neurofeedback who experienced long-term worsening of symptoms.

However, let me frame this answer differently. If you work out at the gym today, your muscles might feel sore later or tomorrow. Is soreness a "side effect?" Most people understand that soreness is a normal part of the process of getting into shape. Soreness usually goes away in a day or two. Heck, you can get tired from studying hard—that's brain exercise, too.

Does anyone ever feel "sore" from a neurofeedback brain workout? ("Sore" is just a metaphor—no one's brain—or head—hurts after doing neurofeedback). Sure, some people can feel a bit "off" after the session. When that happens, I adjust their training next time (or on the spot) to even them out. By the way—you might not notice effects until the next day (just like the gym).

While most people feel better after a session (or notice nothing at all), some find their sleep disturbed or they feel irritable or they have a slight headache. The response is purely from the brain workout. Like a gym workout or concentrating too hard, any effects are usually temporary and go away in a day or two. It's part of the process, particularly if you've just started training. It can take a little time to get used to working out your brain.

A competent neurofeedback provider can adapt the brain workout each session to reduce its intensity or duration, if needed. This is particularly helpful for very sensitive people who may need to go more slowly or lightly in their workout until their brain gets used to it. Conversely, I know providers who don't believe in adjusting the length or type of training from session to session. They feel the brain ends up adapting more quickly and becomes stable faster by steady training. Different providers have different approaches to training, so I encourage you to discuss your concerns with your provider.

I know a few neurofeedback providers who say they rarely have clients who experience any "sore"-type training effects, but I've never figured out how to achieve that myself. It's possible that those providers attract a different type of clientele than we do in my center.

It's unusual for symptoms that arise after a brain training session to last for more than a couple of days. Sometimes some other factor completely independent of the neurofeedback may have caused symptoms.

If symptoms are being stirred up by neurofeedback and don't resolve quickly over several sessions, your provider should consider making changes based on your feedback. This is not a NO PAIN-NO GAIN gym model. That being said, some people have particularly sensitive nervous systems and take longer to find comfortable training.

In many respects, a "sore" response to training is positive. It can indicate that your brain is highly responsive to training.

19. When does neurofeedback not work?

Since neurofeedback does not involve a magic wand, there are potential roadblocks to the successful completion of training.

These include:

- Diet and nutrition (See Appendix for more information)
- "Giving up" due to impatience or inconsistent or slow progress
- Incorrect training protocol(s)
- Certain medications such as benzodiazepines or too many meds
- Alcohol, recreational drug use and other lifestyle factors
- Failure to train regularly
- Environmental issues
- Medical issues
- Family Issues (having poor or no support)

Several of the items above are discussed in more depth within this section.

20. Are there environmental factors that can impact training success?

Yes. Here are some common ones:

- Chronic use of alcohol and drugs, including pot and vaping
- Exposure to mold
- Chronic exposure to paints, chemicals or pesticides, which can impact neurological functioning
- Internet addiction
- Too much cell phone use; sleeping too close to cell phones. There's emerging evidence that microwave frequencies from cell phones and Wi-Fi routers may affect your brain, particularly during sleep when your brain is supposed to recover and recharge
- Poor diet/nutrition

21. Can medical or metabolic factors impact training success?

There are many medical and metabolic factors that can impact training success, but below are several of the most common:

- **Poor gut health.** What does gut health have to do with brain issues? When your gut works better, there's evidence your brain works better.

  In his book *The Mind-Gut Connection*, UCLA physician Emeran Mayer, M.D. discusses how gut health can affect the brain when it comes to conditions like anxiety and depression. Increasing research points to how the microbiome affects the brain. Those conditions can be related to antibiotics or medication use, chronically poor diet, artificial sweeteners, concussions or a hard hit to the head. We frequently recommend that our clients educate themselves about improving their gut health. My experience is that neurofeedback often helps you feel better despite gut problems, but focusing on gut health is important in the long-term.

- **Thyroid issues.** Sometimes undiagnosed thyroid problems contribute to "brain issues." In certain situations, the thyroid impacts brain states such as mood and sleep. If you suspect a thyroid problem but your labs say "normal," you may want to research this issue further or seek out additional testing. Do a search online for "thyroid mental health" to learn more.

- **Hormones.** Hormones can affect mood, sleep and anxiety as a contributor to mental health symptoms and can often be missed, even with tests. For more information, do an internet search using the term "hormones mental health problems."

- Other medical issues that could have an impact: undiagnosed issues with blood sugar stability, hidden food allergies. exposure to toxins in food or environment, excessive histamine response, being on the "wrong" meds, post-anesthesia issues, genetic issues and chronic mold exposure.

22. If neurofeedback is so darn good, why hasn't my doctor or therapist told me about it?

Even though neurofeedback has been around since the 1960s, with numerous studies demonstrating its effectiveness, it still hasn't gained broad acceptance.

There are multiple reasons. Most medical doctors and mental health professionals don't know much about neurofeedback, nor do they understand its implications. It's not a subject they learn in their formal training, so it's not part of their conventional toolbox. Health care providers generally won't recommend a therapy until they feel comfortable with and understand it or until more of their colleagues offer it.

Here's my personal take on some of the other reasons that neurofeedback isn't more widely used:

- Most health care providers don't have time to research neurofeedback well enough to recommend it. There's a big learning curve.

- The technology isn't "ownable" or patentable. This means that no major company (yet) will invest the large sums of money necessary to promote it, educate providers and help it gain acceptance across the health care system.

- Neurofeedback technology crosses numerous academic disciplines. No single discipline claims it (psychology, psychiatry, neurology, special ed, cognitive neuroscience, etc.). As a result, almost no graduate schools or medical schools have taken on the responsibility (opportunity) to educate health professionals about neurofeedback.

- Emphasizing neurofeedback as a treatment (training) of first resort requires a paradigm shift (which isn't easy for professionals) from "treatment" (a.k.a. drugs) to "training."

- Private insurance companies and Medicare have extremely restrictive coverage of neurofeedback—even though there are applicable codes. It would likely take the hiring of expensive lobbyists and more studies to get greater coverage. The industry has been too small to afford that effort. That being said, there seems to be increasing coverage by some insurance companies.

Despite those challenges, a growing number of clinicians are using neurofeedback. Why? Because (1) they hear success stories from other clinicians and their own clients; (2) they've read articles or research; or (3) clients request alternatives to traditional medications.

23. Why don't more health care providers offer neurofeedback?

A significant investment of time and money is required for a health care professional to offer neurofeedback. The provider must learn new technology, a new paradigm about EEG feedback, and how to use neurofeedback to train mood, attention, anxiety, cognitive processing and neurological function.

There's also the element of skepticism and lack of familiarity. Most professionals don' t know enough about neurofeedback's clinical impact to want to offer it or simply don't have time to research and learn it. Those who have taken the time to learn it and see how powerful it can be find it hard to convince their colleagues to do it. Many professionals don't realize how much neurofeedback could benefit certain of their patients.

24. How do I know the improvement was the result of neurofeedback, not other treatments that finally "kicked in?"

Many neurofeedback clients try other approaches to help themselves. If there's a small improvement after adding neurofeedback, and all other efforts have been in place for a while, I assume it's the neurofeedback that produced the recent change. In general, neurofeedback training is synergistic with other treatments. When the brain starts working better from training, *everything* seems to produce better results—including medication, therapy, diet changes, exercise and tutoring.

Identifying progress can be hard when it's gradual and subtle. It's also easy to assign progress to other efforts without realizing the rate of improvement has increased since adding neurofeedback. For example, clients will say, "My child's speech has really improved, the speech therapy has finally kicked in," or "The medications my daughter has been on for six months are finally starting to work," or "My child is finally starting to mature"...but these improvements only occurred after adding neurofeedback to their regimen.

It's helpful to evaluate your progress by asking for input from those around you who know you well—and to keep a log or record of how things were at the beginning. It's hard for anyone to notice minor changes from day to day, because they're subtle. That's why careful tracking and input from others can be essential.

25. Do I have to want to participate in the training for neurofeedback to work?

No. Even adolescents, who are sometimes dragged to their neurofeedback sessions with extreme opposition, respond to training. Thinking that it will work or not work is not a primary factor for success. If you get someone in the room, place the sensors on their head and give them computer-generated feedback, they will generally respond no matter how much they dislike being there.

Some adults with chronic issues believe everything will fail, including neurofeedback. However, this attitude doesn't seem to be a factor influencing their outcome, as long as they continue their training. Your brain responds to feedback whenever you are hooked up to the equipment.

Some people prefer to be involved, pay attention and engage consciously in the training process, while others don't. Some even close their eyes, oblivious to the feedback. Regardless of how it's done, all seem to learn from the training.

Sometimes people come for neurofeedback training because a parent, spouse or another significant person in their life has urged them to go. In our experience, those who do not believe it is going to work are less likely to show up for appointments or stick with the program long enough for the training to be effective, and they are the most likely ones to say "it didn't work." A poor attitude, however, is not the problem. Inconsistent or insufficient training is the bigger problem.

26. Is all neurofeedback the same?

Not all neurofeedback is the same. However, I believe all neurofeedback, when administered by a competent provider, can be helpful.

There are a number of neurofeedback systems and a variety of training models. A training model is defined as an approach to the assessment of the problem, how to target the problem and how to train it with neurofeedback.

There's ongoing debate in the field as to whether some models and systems are better than others for various kinds of problems. There's no clear-cut evidence yet that any one type of feedback is consistently superior to the others (which doesn't mean they are not). It's a difficult issue, even for experienced providers, to compare and sort out. A full discussion is well beyond the scope of this book. In my practice, I use multiple systems and types of models for training, depending on the client's issue.

There are lots of options. Neurofeedback providers can train with systems that use only one EEG channel at a time. Other providers train two, four, seven or nineteen channels at a time. Some providers combine different types of biofeedback or other neuromodulation tools with neurofeedback.

There are practitioners who primarily use qEEG brain maps to drive all training. Other practitioners never use qEEG brain maps but target training based on which region of the brain relates to the client's issues or symptoms. Competent clinicians I know in both groups report they get very good results using their preferred model.

I don't hesitate to refer clients to clinicians I respect, even if they use completely different models than I do. I think that the most important factors are whether they have experience working with a client's issues and if they achieve results consistently using the systems/models they offer. Other colleagues may disagree.

27. Can I do neurofeedback training at home?

The short answer is "yes," but I want to clarify something first.

For neurofeedback training at home, the better question is, even though you *may* find a way to do neurofeedback training at home, *should* you?

If there's a neurofeedback provider fairly close by, there are advantages to going to someone experienced. In theory, you should get higher quality care from someone knowledgeable and experienced. You also may have to do fewer sessions to see results, as they may offer training that is more sophisticated than what you could do on your own.

On the other hand, there are situations where a home system might be worth considering: you're far from a provider or you need neurofeedback sessions over a long period of time, or several times per week, because of complex issues. The problem is that most people don't know how much neurofeedback they will need nor how to do it correctly. The best way to do training at home is with the guidance of an experienced practitioner.

There are simpler tools that can be used at home which impact the brain. They aren't as potent or far-reaching as neurofeedback for brain issues but may be useful. These include heart coherence training or breathing tools, audio-visual entrainment (AVE), sound stimulation technologies, infrared or red-light simulation and pulsed magnetic field (PEMF) devices. An internet search can provide information on these tools.

Some neurofeedback providers, and a small number of companies, offer options for home-based neurofeedback. I suggest you look for a provider who offers good support and is experienced in applying neurofeedback to your type of issue or situation. The provider can answer questions relevant to your response to training, assess progress and help you make decisions about the process.

In my experience, it's often more difficult to do neurofeedback successfully at home than in an office. Home training requires discipline and commitment. It's best done in a positive, supportive environment. Even those who've spent substantial money on home use systems sometimes struggle to follow through over time.

It can be helpful to have a trained professional observing what's occurring during the session, at least periodically. That element may be missing for someone training at home. There are providers who run or monitor home training sessions remotely using a videocam, which addresses or minimizes this issue.

Another factor is that training protocols may occasionally need to be adjusted. Choosing the adjustments is best done with input from someone experienced (this can also be managed remotely). Some systems provide what could be described as self-adjustments. These help, but in my experience, it's hard to completely automate all decisions about training, particularly for people with complex brain issues.

While I've been successful in supporting home users remotely, my success rate is significantly lower than what I see in my office face-to-face. Many of the home users I took on were complex cases to start out with, which makes support more challenging.

More things can get in the way at home, like interruptions or lack of support for what you're doing. It can be easier for the client to get frustrated—or not follow through—or be inconsistent. Sometimes not everyone in the process stays calm or patient, and that can interfere with success.

Purchasing a home unit could end up costing as much as or more than what you would pay doing sessions in a clinical office. You may also incur costs to pay a neurofeedback provider to supervise or direct you.

All that being said, home training can make sense for some people, particularly if there's no provider nearby or when a lot of sessions may be needed.

28. What is a brain map (qEEG) and why have one?

There are many types of brain maps, also called brain scans. The most common are EEG, MRI, PET and SPECT. All maps are designed to give information about the brain and compare it to some type of group norm or average.

The brain map that neurofeedback practitioners most often use to determine training targets is the qEEG (quantitative EEG), which documents the brain's timing and processing speed. The qEEG differs from other types of scans like fMRI, PET and CAT scans because it looks specifically at how neurons are firing, up to hundredths of a second, which seems to correlate to how we think. A qEEG looks at brain processes vs. body processes. Body processes are the most typical use of commonly known brain scanning technology.

Trying to explain the qEEG in any depth is beyond the scope of this book. We'll keep this simple. For more information, search Google or YouTube for "qEEG," go to CenterForBrain.com (click on brain mapping) or search Amazon for books. There are also many qEEG articles on the web.

In simple terms, a qEEG employs software that analyzes and produces statistical properties about a recorded EEG. It uses normative (average) data to compare your EEG with others in your age range. It provides information on neuronal firing patterns. Two important patterns qEEGs may identify are:

- Groups of neurons firing too fast or too slowly compared to the average (norms); where in the brain that "misfiring" occurs; and patterns of excessive fast or slow EEG activity. (All of these contribute to the brain working inefficiently).

- Which parts of your brain aren't "talking" well to other areas. Different parts of your brain are constantly communicating with each other through neuronal signaling. It's a key part of how your brain works. If the timing of the communications is too fast or too slow, or "out of sync," it can interfere drastically with function.

Technical note: Emerging brain research points to the importance of communications across various brain networks or pathways.

The goal is to help providers target the training to problematic areas of the brain that correlate with the client's symptoms or goals.

Think of qEEG brain mapping like having a lab test at your doctor's office. Similar to a medical test, the results don't tell the provider the best way to address the problem but rather provide clues about problem areas. The provider must still make the appropriate training decision about how to best use neurofeedback to target the issue.

Over the last 15 years, I've used at least nine different types of qEEG maps. The information and analysis that provide insights about how the brain performs keeps evolving. There's debate within the field about the best mapping options and approaches to using qEEG analysis information. Since each has its pros and cons, it's difficult to sort out. If you want a qEEG map, you'll need to find a provider to rely on who is experienced with brain mapping and its use to help guide neurofeedback.

29. Is a brain map necessary to do neurofeedback?

There's major disagreement in our field about this issue.

There are clinical providers who require a full EEG and/or qEEG brain map to do neurofeedback. They argue one can't effectively assess the brain without that level of information.

Other providers don't use qEEGs at all. They train with neurofeedback based on an understanding of brain function. They target symptoms related to key areas of the brain—for example, the temporal lobe for emotional control, anterior cingulate for obsession/worry or the parietal lobe for sensory integration. They may use information in the EEG at the sites they train to help guide some aspects of training.

At our center, we recommend qEEGs on a case-by-case basis, taking into consideration the client's history, symptoms and budget and our experience with the problem. I typically use a qEEG for clients with long or complicated histories or those with learning disabilities, cognitive issues, concussions and seizures. Brain maps *can* speed up training for certain clients but in my experience don't always do so. It depends on various factors. Many of my clients request a brain map because they like knowing more about what's going on in their brain.

When I train clients without a map, I target key regions in the brain that correlate to their symptoms and make adjustments as necessary. I'm able to do this because neurofeedback equipment has monitors that show the client's EEG (the electrical activity in their brain at any given moment). These clients usually have good outcomes, too.

I believe training with or without qEEG maps can be effective when applied by a competent neurofeedback professional. I have colleagues on both sides of that fence. Some will definitely disagree with me.

30. Where can I find the best neurofeedback practitioner?

It's easier to tell you the best *way* to find a neurofeedback provider. Start by asking your mental health or health care professional, and friends. They may have recommendations. The fastest way to find someone in your area is to do an online search using the term "neurofeedback," along with your zip code or city. There's no one website that list all practitioners.

Here are some links for identifying potential providers:

- isnr.org/member-list. International Society for Neurofeedback and Research. Member organization for neurofeedback professionals.
- bcia.org. Certification organization for biofeedback and neurofeedback.
- qeegcertificationboard.org. Certification for qEEG
- AAPB.org. Member organization for biofeedback and neurofeedback professionals

A number of neurofeedback equipment vendors list providers who use their systems or register for their website. Some even have their own private certification for using their equipment.

Finding the best—that's harder. Obviously, you should check their experience, background, credentials, how long they've done neurofeedback, how much neurofeedback they've done with your kind of problem and perhaps their approach to training and working with clients. You may ask some of the questions in this section to see how they respond. You can check online for information about them or speak to them by phone or face-to-face. In the U.S., HIPAA privacy rules restrict providers from giving you the names of clients with whom they have worked, though you can always ask. My main advice—make sure they are a good fit for you.

If no provider is nearby, here are some ideas to consider:

1. Consider driving farther than you would like to, if that will take you to the office of a good provider. It's not uncommon for some clients to drive 1.5 hours to be trained. While a minimum of once a week is ideal, discuss with your provider whether you could benefit from coming every other week. Steady and frequent training is ideal, of course, but it's not the only way. Each situation is unique.

2. Consider an "intensive." Some providers do a lot of sessions in a short time for people who travel a distance to see them and stay locally during a series of sessions, if appropriate.

3. Find a provider who offers remote neurofeedback training at home.

4. Look for alternatives to neurofeedback (light or sound stimulation devices and heart coherence training are examples, but there is much more available). These devices can provide some benefit at a lower cost and far more simply. They aren't as powerful as neurofeedback but can be helpful, depending on the problem.

Describing those alternatives goes beyond the scope of this book.

5. Ask every local clinician or health provider who will listen if they could help bring neurofeedback to your town. I guarantee that others need it in your area. Sometimes a little encouragement or pleading can go a long way. I've seen providers in very small towns who thrived. Small towns have much better word-of-mouth than larger cities.

Numerous types of clinicians can potentially offer neurofeedback: licensed mental health counselors, psychologists, social workers, R.N.s, speech therapists, occupational therapists, special ed teachers, chiropractors and more. A small but growing number of physicians now offer it.

Part 4

Epilogue—Comments and Observations

Helping people function better and overcome serious issues with their brains has become my consuming passion. I have some equally passionate colleagues around the world. We often exchange information and offer encouragement and support to one another as we aim toward the same goal: learning the best ways to help someone's brain and life. Being part of this worldwide community helps us all be better. It's an incredibly caring group of professionals.

I get huge satisfaction watching children and adults begin to manage their lives better and overcome challenging—and sometimes crippling—issues. As their brain works more efficiently, they achieve more and struggle less. It's gratifying when clients tell me how much neurofeedback has improved how they feel and/or allowed them to reduce or get off their meds.

Some clients have very challenging brains

I see my share of challenging clients—clients who don't make progress as quickly or as consistently as my other clients do. When there are ups and downs, it's easy for them to want to give up. They'll say things like, "I don't know if neurofeed-back can work for me." They often don't believe they can change. Experts have told them they require medication.

I try really hard to not let people give up on their brain. The moment they slip or feel like there's little progress, it's almost like they say, "see, I can't do it." But no one gets good at any-thing all at once. Everyone needs encouragement and under-standing to work through it. I've witnessed extremely challenging clients succeed when they were willing to hang in with training. When you see children and adults make sig-nificant improvements with rage, seizures, ADHD, OCD, au-tism, anxiety, and far more…you realize the brain has an amazing capacity for change.

Coaching and encouragement may be the most important role

Getting the right encouragement *is critical* to succeeding at anything, including neurofeedback.

How many people quit the gym before they get into good shape? It's estimated that 80% of those who join quit within a few months. Working out (just like neurofeedback) takes commitment.

A good trainer encourages you to stay with it.

A good trainer encourages you to "push through" the rough patches—without *judgment*.

A good trainer adjusts your training along the way and suggests things you can do outside the gym to achieve your goal.

As a brain coach, I do the same. I try to encourage each cli-ent to hang in there if they hit ups and downs and want to quit. Encouragement from a good friend or family member can also be equally important during this process.

I adjust training protocols as needed. I make suggestions about things that can be done outside of our office regarding diet, lifestyle and environment. I may suggest tools to use at home to help maximize the benefits of neurofeedback training.

Troubleshooting the brain is complicated

When someone's not making steady progress or is having a lot of ups and downs, does that mean the person needs to train more or have different protocols? Maybe the problem is a factor outside of neurofeedback training.

The true problem can be hard to figure out at times. Some contributing factors are invisible, but significant, such as life stresses (job, relationships, bullying), hidden food allergies, childhood trauma, herbicides, an unbalanced microbiome, exposure to chemicals, an out-of-whack thyroid, EMFs and more. It's easy to drive myself nuts trying to put together the puzzle pieces.

I still expect the brain doing neurofeedback to become more stable, but in dealing with outside factors, it may take longer or be more complicated.

A brief example: I had a client with a lifetime of issues. He had numerous ups and downs during training. It took us more than 30 sessions to figure out training that consistently helped his symptoms. He would do extremely well after a session for 6-48 hours before his symptoms crept back. His brain (not neurofeedback) was able to make him feel better consistently for a period of time but just not keep it there.

It turned out he lived in a house with toxic mold and didn't know it. It appears mold exposure kept his brain from holding its gains unless he trained often. With additional support from a physician who understood mold, he's now dramatically better. He attributes neurofeedback and other neuroregulation tools to keeping him sane during an incredibly stressful time. It also helped him sort out the other issues (and to understand that he wasn't just crazy). Many of his gains from neurofeedback returned when his mold exposure was eliminated.

Frustration: So many people can't access neurofeedback

There are so many people who desperately need neurofeedback who don't have access to it or can't afford it. Even though there are signs that neurofeedback is becoming more accessible and that more providers are offering it, there's still a long way to go.

Why do I care? Because there are critical issues in our society that neurofeedback could impact if it were more widely available and accepted.

- There's a huge addiction crisis that is enormously underserved.

- There's an epidemic of anxiety, panic attacks and depression. Many people are on medications but still struggle with symptoms.

- Post-concussion syndrome is massively under-diagnosed by health professionals[16]. It's called a silent epidemic. The effects can occur months or years later and never be identified. This syndrome impacts mental health, personality and cognitive issues. Many people's lives are dramatically impacted by a rear-end crash, a fall, something that fell on them or getting hit by something or someone. Often, they get an MRI and are told they're fine, yet the MRI is not a test for concussion. No one tells the patient about possible follow-up effects.

- Neurofeedback can help significantly in post-concussion syndrome. Clinical reports from hundreds of clinicians show consistently positive improvements.

Unfortunately, the research is limited, in large part because there's been little funding for it.

Health professionals who offer neurofeedback see it improving outcomes *consistently* in all these areas, but there's no mechanism for scaling it. Yet the technology is scalable.

What would it take for neurofeedback to grow rapidly as a field?

It's hard to imagine that the solution to growing neurofeedback will come from within the health care system. If it could, it probably would have happened by now. *Extreme innovation will be required to scale its impact on mental health, learning issues and neurological disorders.*

---

[16] https://www.sciencedaily.com/releases/2013/10/131010124740.htm

Neurofeedback needs a hero to come along to fund the education, research and infrastructure required to impact the medical community and the general public.

I believe neurofeedback's best chance of rapid growth would come from a major high-tech company, a foundation outside of health care or perhaps "angel" social impact investors.

Whether one of those organizations or individuals will step up to leverage the potential of this technology is anybody's guess. If that were to happen, neurofeedback could be a game-changer for so many people.

Neurofeedback is gaining traction as more people search online

The brain is a hot topic in the news and in books, articles and scientific research. PBS has been educating the public with shows by psychiatrist Daniel Amen, M.D., who talks about brain scans, and neuroscientist Michael Merzenich, Ph.D., who talks about neuroplasticity. Neurologist David Perlmutter, M.D. talks about options to medications, including food. Dr. Mehmet Oz does segments about the brain and brain health on his popular TV show.

As more people investigate these "brain oriented" alternatives to medications online, many stumble across neurofeedback. Hopefully, that eventually translates into more providers exploring neurofeedback for their own practices.

Am I optimistic about the future of neurofeedback?

Yes, I am. Two areas where it's becoming a more commonplace option (or at least there's more awareness) is in the treatment of PTSD and addiction.

PTSD/Trauma treatment

I attribute the growing use of neurofeedback in trauma therapy in part to two popular books that contain sections about neurofeedback's impact on trauma.

The first is *The Body Keeps the Score: Brain, Mind, and Body in the Healing of Trauma* by psychiatrist Bessel van der Kolk.

Dr. van der Kolk is a psychiatrist well-known by many trauma therapists. He has lectured worldwide on the role of neurofeedback in trauma, which also has increased its visibility.

The other book is *Neurofeedback in the Treatment of Developmental Trauma: Calming the Fear-Driven Brain* by Sebern Fisher. This book is more targeted to therapists than the general public but does a remarkable job of explaining the impact of neurofeedback on trauma. Sebern Fisher also does quite a bit of lecturing about the impact on trauma.

Published studies by Dr. Ruth Lanius, a Harvard-trained psychiatrist, and others, are also providing solid research on the basis of neurofeedback in trauma.

Addiction treatment

A small but growing number of drug and alcohol rehabilitation centers have added neurofeedback to their programs. They are learning that it can help improve client outcomes and the likelihood of people staying longer in treatment. Longer stays in treatment give clients a better chance to succeed as they practice stabilizing their brain activity. There's published research that backs this up.

More acceptance from the medical community and more public curiosity and demand

Neurofeedback clinicians around the world report that more medical doctors and mental health professionals are referring patients to them for neurofeedback, particularly those who are not doing well on medications or don't want to be on medications.

Providers are also getting more calls directly from people seeking an alternative to medications. They find neurofeedback either from friends or, very often, from internet research.

Help spread the word

The primary reason I wrote *Neurofeedback 101* was to help people better understand this powerful technology. I hope you'll share this book with friends, relatives and professionals.

It should prompt discussions about what's possible. I hope the day will come, sooner rather than later, when neurofeedback will be a commonplace option for treating brain-based conditions.

I am happy to hear from readers. Feel free to contact me with your questions and comments at Book@CenterForBrain.com. We receive a lot of email, so please be patient if you don't receive an immediate response.

Speaking Engagements

I enjoy speaking about neurofeedback and am glad to discuss speaking opportunities to help educate people about neurofeedback.

I also have access to a network of top health professionals in our field, both in the U.S. and abroad, who like to talk about neurofeedback and its impact.

You can inquire at Book@CenterForBrain.com.

Diet, Supplements and How Hidden Allergies Can Affect Neurofeedback

Poor diet, such as excessive sugar, refined carbohydrates, junk food, unhealthy fats and artificial sweeteners, may slow the progress of neurofeedback training. These foods can compromise your brain's functioning. A better diet and the right supplements can play a stabilizing role, particularly when combined with neurofeedback. While good supplements are helpful, they can't completely overcome a bad diet. See below for supplements I particularly like.

Unidentified food allergies or food sensitivities are common among a significant percentage of our clients. Many of them are unaware that certain foods can trigger issues with mood, behavior, sleep, anxiety and mental clarity. Dairy, wheat, and certain nuts are common hidden allergens, but any food may be problematic. You might eat it every day yet not notice it's a problem, because the response is delayed. (Your body gets used to things that aren't good for it.)

Food allergies can sometimes slow neurofeedback progress or make progress more inconsistent, so we encourage our clients to become their own detectives to rule out issues. Food elimination diets and blood tests can help.

Example: The parents of a ten-year-old girl reported dramatic behavioral strides with neurofeedback after her family took her off dairy for three weeks. As soon as they added dairy back in, she slid backwards—not all the way—but there was an unmistakable difference. Both parents could see the change clearly. It's cases like these that prompt us to consider diet as a possible impediment to progress.

FYI: There are many food allergy tests available. The problem I've heard from clients, and even from physicians, is that the results from different food allergy tests can be inconsistent. However, they can still be useful if you find a provider who has good success with them. New updated tests continue to come out.

On the other hand, food elimination diets provide a more consistent, accurate result, but you have to become your own detective and put more effort into it. We often recommend having the entire family do an elimination diet at the same time. You will find a link to instructions for conducting a food elimination diet in the footnote below.[17]

---

[17] https://www.fammed.wisc.edu/files/webfm-uploads/documents/outreach/im/handout_elimination_diet_patient.pdf

Our experience with supplements and diet for ADHD, "anxious-worried," anxiety, mood issues and obsessive-compulsive disorder

It took me 15 years to find supplements I could offer clients that consistently speed progress with neurofeedback. At our center I often use supplements to help support people trying to lower their medications or enhance their training. (My experience suggests that better brain nutrition can speed up training or help produce stability faster.

Over the past seven years I've recommended two supplements that work for 65-70 percent of those who take them consistently for 30-45 days. They're primarily for clients with mood issues, obsessive thinking, anxiety, worry or ADHD:

- Total Amino Solutions by Genesa Living[18]
- Hardy Nutritionals Daily Essential Nutrients[19]

Over the years, I've noted that many clients taking these supplements need fewer neurofeedback sessions. These supplements may work equally work well with other conditions, but those we've tested are listed above.

Although each supplement can be effective on its own, together they seem to have a synergistic effect, performing better and more consistently than others I've tried. Both companies describe a "micro-nutrient" formulation designed to encourage extremely efficient absorption. The typical dosage is two capsules twice daily, although some clients require more or less for optimal benefit.

---

[18] https://www.genesaliving.com
[19] https://www.hardynutritionals.com

You can learn more about them at the companies' websites. The Hardy supplement has *interesting independent research, which is the reason I checked them out. Few supplements have good independent research.*

You can order these supplements from our clinic, on our website or find them online.

There are, of course, many other supplements I haven't tested.

General diet advice

Even the best supplements can't overcome the harm done by an unhealthy diet, no matter how much neurofeedback you do. (That's like going to the gym daily and eating dinner every night at a fast food restaurant.)

There are a number of nutritional factors that we know can positively impact brain health These include an anti-inflammatory diet (perhaps one of the most important factors) and a healthy gut. Inflammation is an enemy of the brain and the gut. A discussion about those issues goes well beyond the scope of this book, so I encourage you to do further investigation into this arena.

Two experts I follow are Dean Ornish, M.D. and David Perlmutter, M.D.

Dr. Ornish has developed the Ornish Diet, aimed at improving heart and brain health. This diet is approved and covered by Medicare for heart health but goes far beyond that. His book, *Undo It!: How Simple Lifestyle Changes Can Reverse Most Chronic Diseases,* is a good tool for improving brain health.

Dr. Perlmutter is a neurologist and author of the book *Brain Maker. Brain Maker* does a good job of explaining the relationship between the gut and the brain and provides detailed, simple explanations of things you can do to protect your brain and improve your gut.

Other experts who focus on healthy eating whom I particularly like are Dhru Purohit (Broken Brain podcast), Mark Hyman, M.D., Daniel Amen M.D, and Michael Greger, M.D.

About the Author

Michael P. "Mike" Cohen is Director and Chief of Neurotechnology at the Center for Brain Training in Jupiter, Florida, one of the largest neurofeedback practices in South Florida. He has specialized in neurofeedback and helping individuals regulate brain function since 1996.

The Center for Brain Training provides brain and qEEG assessments, neurofeedback, biofeedback and other neuroregulation tools. Mike has a reputation for tackling complex cases that challenge other health care providers. He is considered an expert in the field of neurofeedback. Mike provides support and consultation to physicians, mental health professionals and users of neurofeedback to help them learn to use it effectively.

Since 1998, Mike has taught both basic and advanced neurofeedback courses to several thousand health care and mental health professionals from around the world. He teaches the introductory, in-person **Neurofeedback 101**, the advanced online course, **Neurofeedback 201** and an online **Alpha Theta Basics** course. These courses are primarily for health and education professionals but also attract people in the general public interested in learning more about neuroplasticity and neurofeedback.

Acknowledgments

Conceiving of, organizing, writing, re-writing, polishing and actually *finishing* a book is a daunting task—more daunting than I realized when I embarked on the adventure of creating *Neurofeedback 101*. It's said that "it takes a village," and that was certainly true with this project.

So many people contributed ideas, information, inspiration and support that it's hard to name them all.

I first want to acknowledge the unwavering and patient support of my business and life partner, Carolyn Cohen, who has been by my side since 1986. She has also managed my practice over the years while I learned and perfected my neurofeedback knowledge and skill, always looking out for my best interests.

I want to acknowledge Gwen Carden, my editor, who has been with me throughout the writing part of this journey. She's fixed up my grammar, my spelling, reeled my prose back down to earth and helped to organize my thoughts into a logical flow.

I also want to acknowledge Dr. Elizabeth "Liz" Doyle, the Center for Brain Training's Director of Education, who has been a key player in growing the scope of my professional teaching department. She has skillfully brought through my office doors numerous health care and neurofeedback providers seeking training. They made me a better teacher and indirectly contributed to the principles found in this book.

There have been many colleagues from around the world who have taught me, shared with me, brainstormed with me and inspired me. There are too many to mention, but I feel particularly indebted to: Ed Hamlin, Glenn Weiner, Larry Hirshberg, Moshe Perl, Sebern Fisher, Jay Gunkelman, Barry Sterman, Howard and Patti Lightstone, Rob Coben, Roger DeBeus, Joel Lubar, Mark Smith, Ray McGarty, Matt Fleischman, Joy Lunt, the late Jack Johnstone, Bill Scott, Neil King, Siegfried and Sue Othmer, Les Fehmi, Marty Wuttke, Martijn Arns, and Juri Kropotov.

And then there are my clients—thousands of them—who've shared their challenges, unimaginable hardships and heroic victories with me. They've kept me motivated as I see them struggle—and in many cases succeed—at improving their lives. They have also taught me to be a better neurofeedback practitioner and a more caring person.

And thanks to Evan and Scott of the boys breakfast club who helped keep me motivated.

For each of those people, and others too numerous to mention, I am profoundly grateful.

Made in United States
Orlando, FL
21 July 2023